KU-684-000

Geoffrey the Tube Train and the Fat Comedian

Text by Alexei Sayle
Pictures by Oscar Zarate
Lettering and typographical design by Trevs Phoenix

First published in Great Britain in 1987
by Methuen London Ltd
11 New Fetter Lane, London EC4P 4EE

Copyright © Alexei Sayle and Oscar Zarate 1987

British Library Cataloguing in Publication Data

Sayle, Alexei
Geoffrey the tube train and the fat
comedian.
1. English wit and humour, Pictorial
I. Title II. Zarate, Oscar
741.5'942 NC1479

ISBN 0-413-59950-7

Printed in Great Britain

This book is sold subject to the condition that it shall not, by way of trade or otherwise, be lent, resold, hired out, or otherwise circulated without the publisher's prior consent in any form of binding or cover other than that in which it is published and without a similar condition being imposed upon the subsequent publisher.

ACKNOWLEDGEMENTS

Many thanks for help received to: Hazel Hirshorn and Albert Price,
O.Z.

Also by Alexei Sayle and published by Methuen

TRAIN TO HELL

A Methuen Paperback

GEOFFREY THE TUBE TRAIN AND THE FAT COMEDIAN

Being as ow I'm just an umble stand up comedian I ain't much good wif the written word like. Not like them writin' toffs, yer Doris Lessins or A.N. Wilsons. Nevertheless I want to write about the summer when I was all washed up on the shores of light entertainment,If I could just locate them right words, I knows, I could make it come real alive on the page.....
So, here goes.......It was summer in London. It was quite hot and sort of

8

STOP
SCHOOL
CHILDREN
LONDON
8

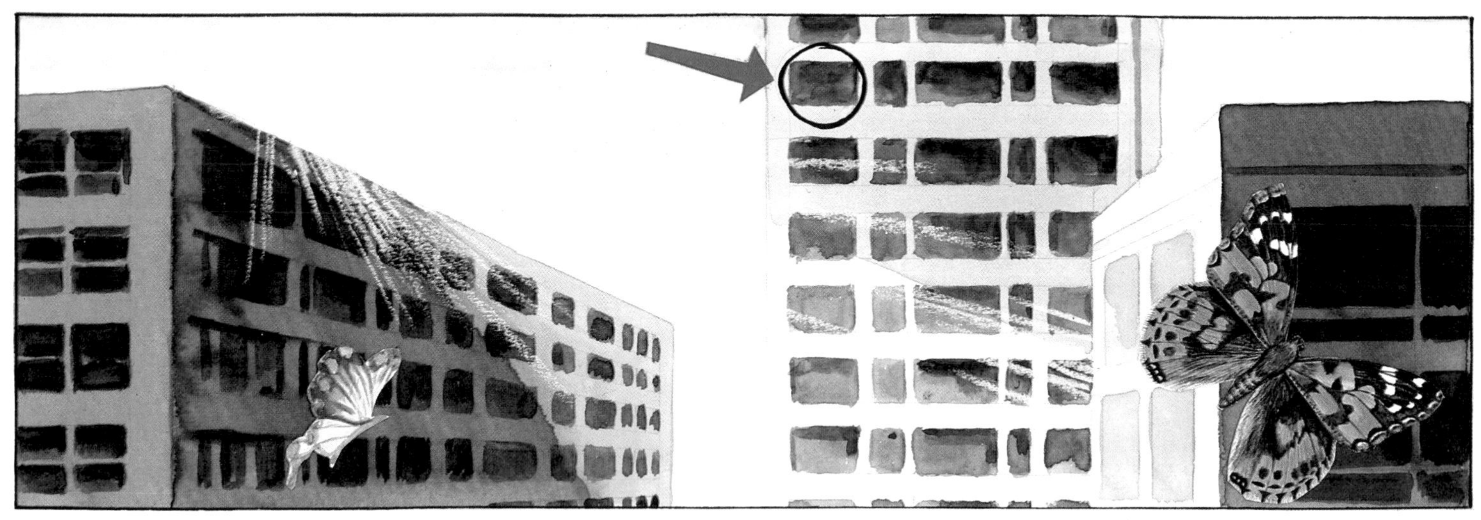

DOING SOLITARY IN MY TOWER BLOCK. I JUST COULDN'T BE FUNNY. NO I HADN'T LOST IT.* BUT THERE WAS THIS INJUNCTION SEE...

HAPPENS ALL THE TIME IN THE ROCK BIZ. ONE SPLIT SECOND AN ACT IS HOT HOT HOT, THE NEXT GONE GONE GONE. THE REASON - INJUNCTIONS. GLENN MILLER, ELVIS PRESLEY AND JOSEPH STALIN AREN'T DEAD. THEY'RE LIVING IN A MOTEL IN BASILDON WAITING FOR INJUNCTIONS FROM THEIR MANAGERS TO COME BEFORE COLCHESTER SMALL CLAIMS COURT.

IT'S ALWAYS THE MANAGER, THE PAID FRIEND, WHO DOES IT. I KNEW THAT BEFORE I STARTED. I THOUGHT I WAS CLEVER, I COULD AVOID ALL THAT.

*FOOTNOTE "Losing it" is the event most feared, of the many things comedians fear. The ability to create laughter is an intangible thing and comics dread that one day, it may just vanish. You lose that essential empathy with your audience -you dozy shitbag-and you also lose your TI......M......ING. The most celebrated recorded example of "losing it" happened in 1921 to the veteran music hall patter-man Albert "Oo wants to see me luvverley cockles" Magoogle. Closing the half at the Bristol Hippodrome a small pink light was seen to exit from his right ear. From that moment until his death six years later when he was on stage, he could only ever talk about balsa wood in an impenetrable Swansea accent.

BUT JUST AS A NEW-WAVE COMEDY SPAWNED NEW-WAVE VENUES, IT ALSO SPAWNED NEW-WAVE SHARKS AND THE ONE I SIGNED WITH WAS THE ALTERNATIVE EQUIVALENT OF A GIANT KILLER WHITE.

HIS NAME WAS MR SAUNDERS. HE APPROACHED ME AT SOME BENEFIT. SAID I NEEDED A MANAGER. MAKE ME A STAR.

AT THE TIME HE SEEMED A NICE GUY - SURELY HE WOULDN'T RIP ME OFF. AFTER ALL, THE GUY WAS LEFT -WING - THEN, SO WAS POL POT. THE CONTRACT I SIGNED WAS THE SAME TEN-YEAR-ONE THE P.O.W.s ON THE CHANGI RAILROAD SIGNED. AFTER THREE YEARS OF EXPLOITATION I TOLD MR SAUNDERS TO PISS OFF....

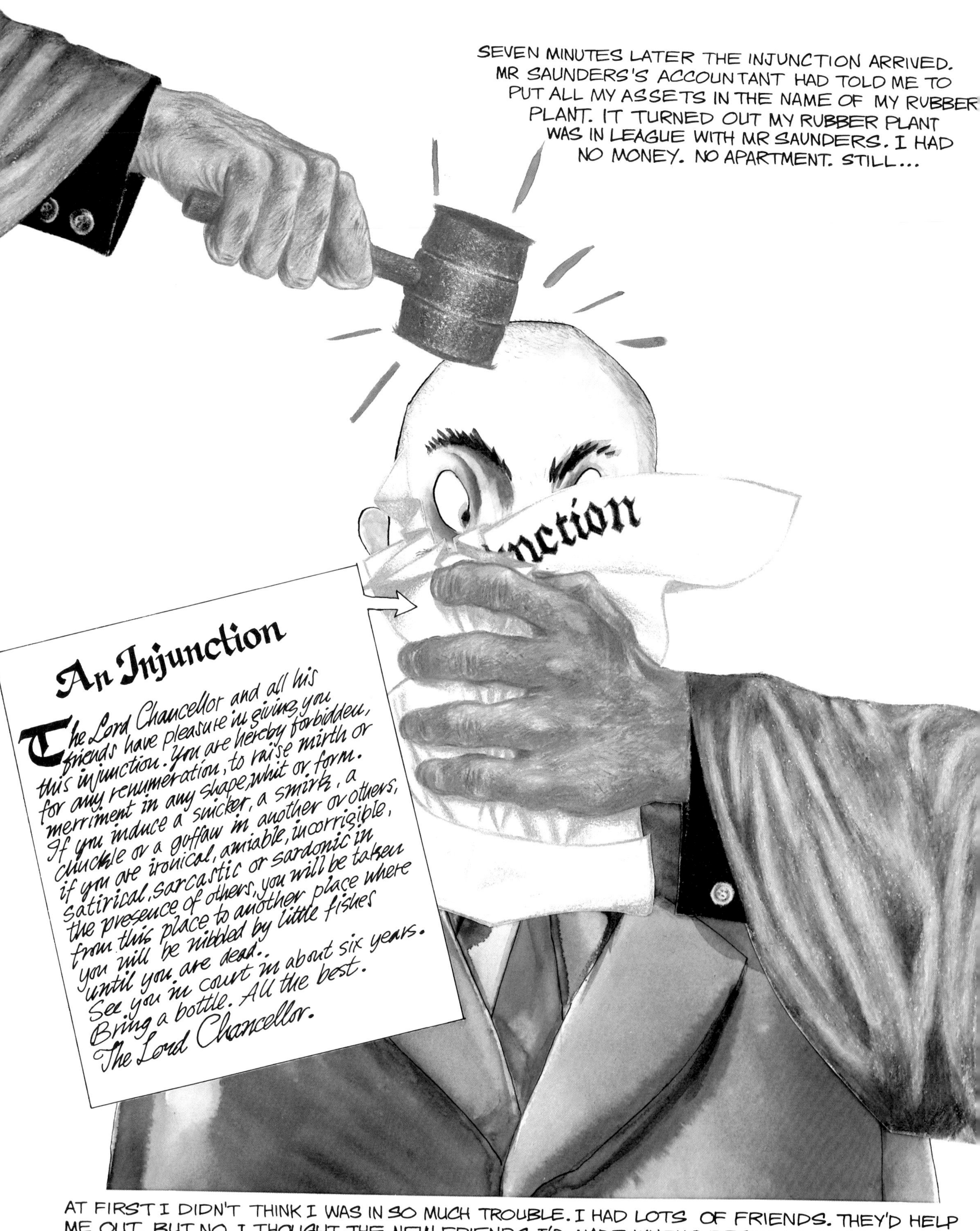

AT FIRST I DIDN'T THINK I WAS IN SO MUCH TROUBLE. I HAD LOTS OF FRIENDS. THEY'D HELP ME OUT. BUT NO. I THOUGHT THE NEW FRIENDS I'D MADE WHEN I BECAME A SUCCESSFUL PERFORMER WOULD BE JUST LIKE MY OLD PALS, ONLY RICHER AND MORE TALENTED. VERY FUNNY. EITHER SOMETHING HAPPENS TO PEOPLE ON THE STAIRWAY TO THE STARS OR, MORE LIKELY, PEOPLE WHO SUCCEED IN SHOW BUSINESS ALWAYS WERE MORE SNOBBISH, VAIN, EGOTISTICAL AND MONOMANIACAL THAN NORMAL FOLKS. THEY CERTAINLY FEAR THAT FAILURE IS CONTAGIOUS. I HAD AN HYSTERICAL VISION OF MYSELF AS SOME KIND OF INFECTED PORK PIE SPOILING THE PARTY FOR EVERYONE ELSE. I COULD SEE I MADE MY NEW PALS FIDGETY, SO I CUT MYSELF OFF FROM THE COMPANY OF COMEDIANS.

FORTUNATELY SOME REAL OLD FRIENDS, FROM MY POLITICAL DAYS* MANAGED TO GET ME A JOB WITH A FLAT. I WAS TO BE COMEDIAN IN RESIDENCE ON THE BLUEBIRD FARM ESTATE IN NORTH LONDON. MONDAY AFTERNOONS WAS LENNY BRUCE FOR THE OVER-NINETIES. TUESDAY MORNINGS WAS COMMEDIA DELL' ARTE FOR MUMS 'N TINY TOTS.

*FOOTNOTE. From the age of seven I was a member of the Merseyside branch of the Communist Party of Britain (Marxist-Leninist) - the CPB(M-L) which, in the infinitely fissionable world of left-wing politics had been a splinter of the Communist Party of Great Britain - CPGB. The CPB(M-L) itself then split into the Communist Party of England (Marxist-Leninist) - CPE(M-L). That group split over lunch into the Communist Party of England (Marxist-Florist) - CPE(M-F) and were rumoured to be receiving cash from that sinister pan-national organisation Interflora. The Marxist-Florists and the Communist Party of Leicester (Marxist-Shopping list) - CPL(M-S) inevitably split into the Communist Federation of Islington (Maxist-Wallist) - CFI(M-W). They then of course split and became "Fat Larry's Band" who had a big hit in 1979 with "Zoom" which was number one all over Europe and America.

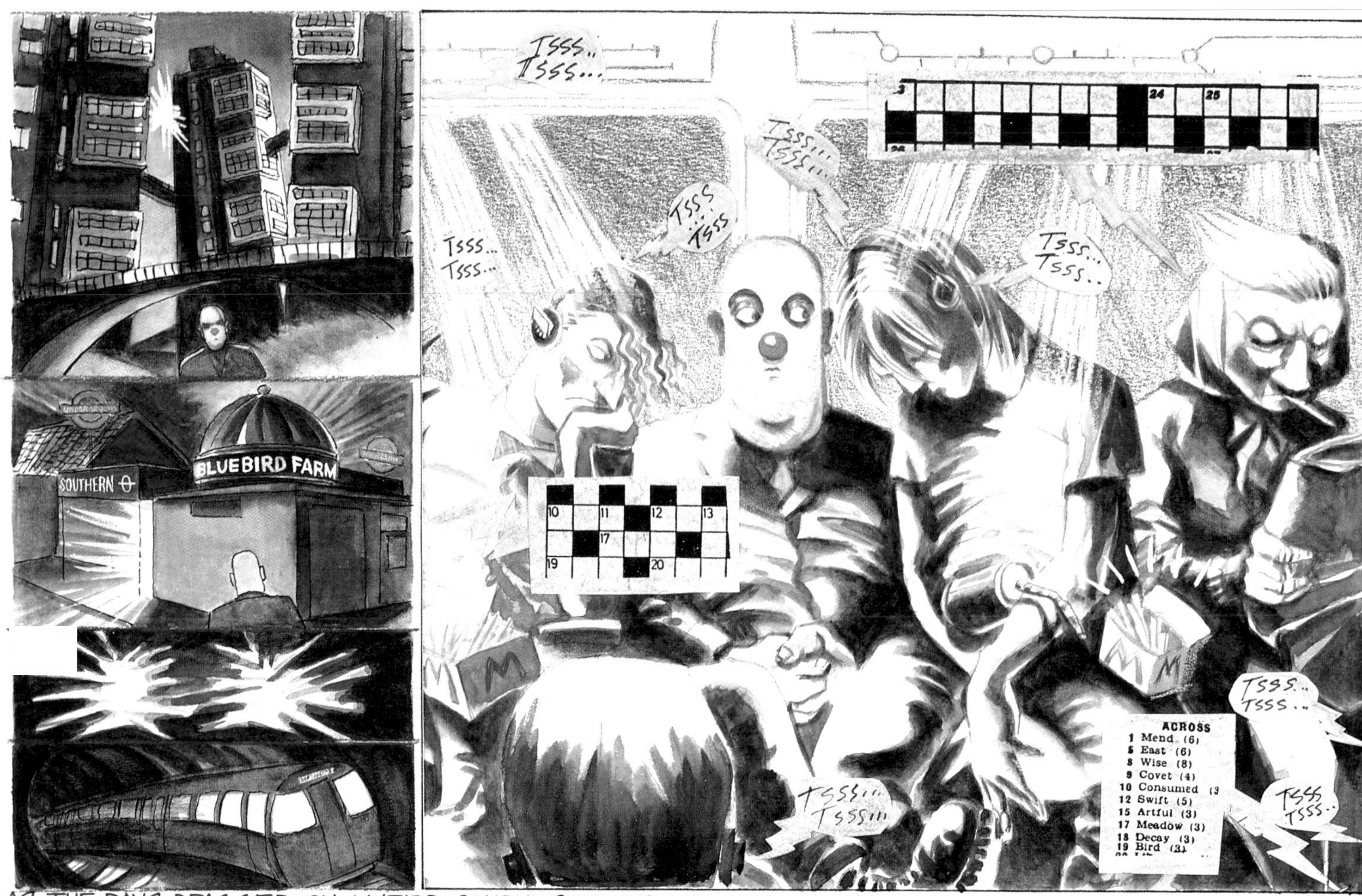

AS THE DAYS DRAGGED ON A WEIRD COMPULSION STOLE OVER ME. WHEN I HAD BEEN FREE TO PERFORM, I NEVER EVER WANTED TO. NOW THAT I COULDN'T, I WAS DESPERATE TO GET ON ANY STAGE. MOST NIGHTS, HEAVILY DISGUISED, I CAUGHT THE TUBE TO ONE OF THE THOUSANDS OF COMEDY CLUBS THAT HAD SPRUNG UP IN THE LAST COUPLE OF YEARS - LAFF RIOT COMEDY WORKSHOP AT BOWGLERS CABARET, UPSTAIRS AT JANGLERS PUB 'N PATISSERIE IN NEW STOKINGTON HIGH STREET.

MY MOTTO IN SHOW BUSINESS HAD ALWAYS BEEN "NEVER BE NICE TO ANYBODY ON THE WAY UP BECAUSE I'M NOT COMING DOWN AGAIN."
NOW HERE I WAS DOWN AT THE ROCKIEST BOTTOM.

EVEN WHEN I GOT ON STAGE MY PROBLEMS WEREN'T OVER. TRY AS HARD AS I MIGHT TO DO A PROPER ACT, ONCE IN THE SPOTLIGHT MY MOUTH WOULD TALK ABOUT NOTHING BUT MY LEGAL PROBLEMS.

LONDON IS A CITY OF TRIBES. THE TRIBE HERE TONIGHT HAD ONCE FLOURISHED ALL OVER THE CITY BUT LIKE ANCIENT CELTS THEY'D NOW BEEN BEATEN BACK TO DISTANT CORNERS OF NORTH LONDON.

THIS TRIBE PUT A LOT OF STORE IN WORDS. IF YOU SAID THE WRONG WORDS IT WAS BAD MAGIC. THEY BECAME VERY CROSS.

COR' THESE PEOPLE HAVE GOT NO SENSE OF HUMOUR.

A TYPICAL NIGHT OUT FOR ME THESE DAYS. SOMETHING HAD TO CHANGE.

THROUGH THAT HOT NIGHT I REALIZED I NEEDED TO DO SOMETHING MORE WITH MY TIME, TO FILL UP THE EMPTY DAYS AND NIGHTS.

A BOOK! THEY COULDN'T STOP ME WRITING A BOOK AND AFTER THE LEGAL TROUBLE WAS OVER IT COULD B PUBLISHED. BUT WHAT SORT OF BOOK? FOR A WHILE I HAD WORKED ON A COOKBOOK FOR ROCK PEOPLE ON THE ROAD, STAYING IN HOTELS - HOW TO COOK MOULES MARINIÈRE IN A CORBY TROUSER PRESS, THAT KIND OF THING. THAT WAS NO GOOD.

T HAD TO BE A CHANGE OF DIRECTION, MAYBE SOMETHING HARMLESS, SOMETHING THAT WOULD MAKE ME LOOK PLEASANT TO ALL THE IMPORTANT SHOWBIZ PEOPLE THAT I'D UPSET. THEN IT HIT ME - A CHILDREN'S BOOK!

TOWARDS DAWN I GOT MY PAINTS OUT AND BY MID-MORNING THERE WAS...

Geoffrey was a happy Tube train. "Clackety-Clack" sang Geoffrey.

"Clickety-Click" sang Geoffrey's driver. He was called Driver Bob.

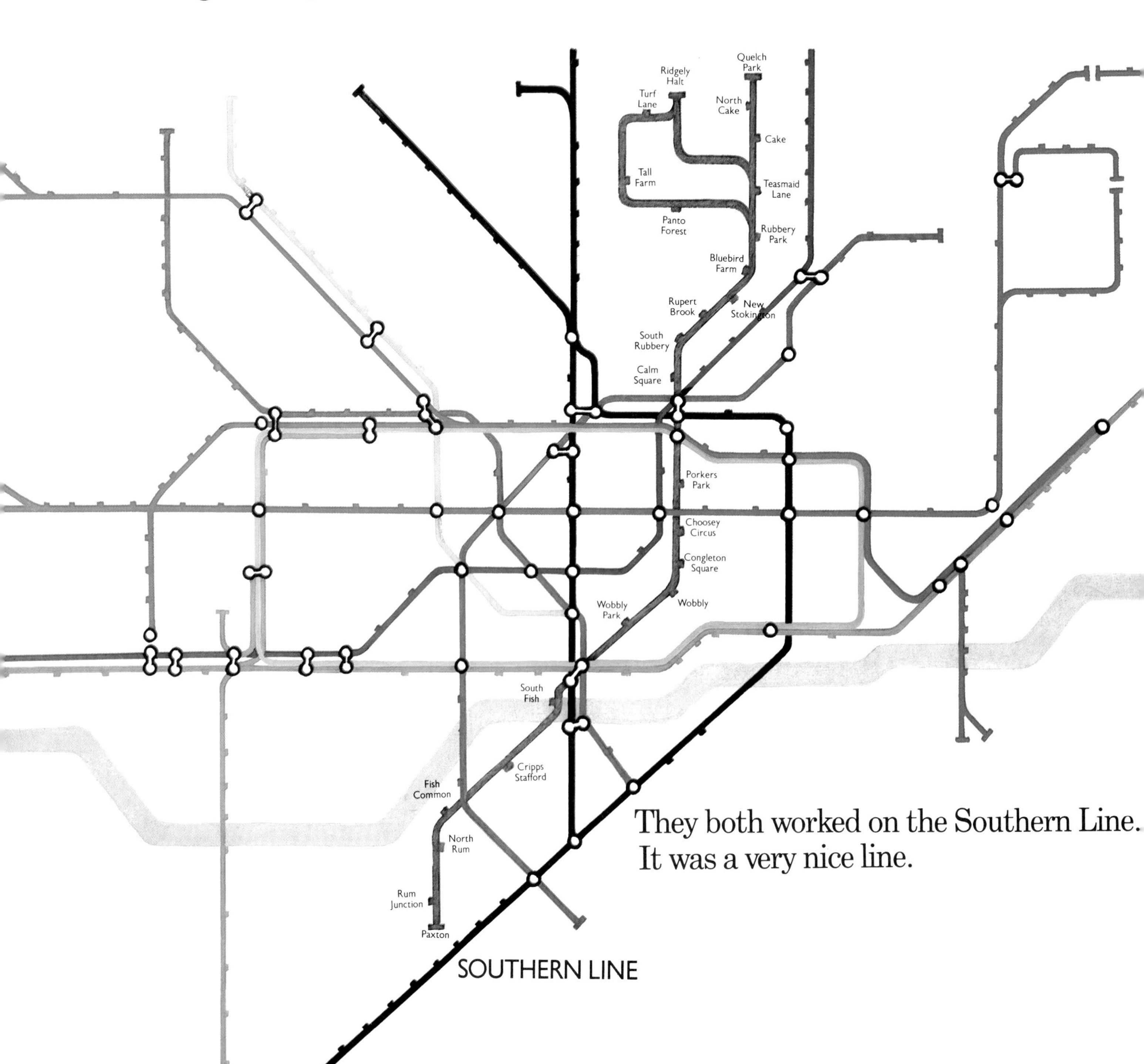

They both worked on the Southern Line. It was a very nice line.

It went from Quelch Park in the north, where all the kind white people with the new German cars lived...

to Paxton in the south, where all the nice black people with the old British cars lived.

On the way it passed through New Stokington where all the nice young middle-class people were moving in and the comedians used to make jokes about them all, knocking their front and back room into one in the same week and the street falling down and they thought it was jolly funny and moved in anyway.

MID-MORNING. I LOOKED AT WHAT I'D DONE. I WAS REALLY PLEASED, A PERFECT KID'S BOOK, SOPPY AND HARMLESS. THEY COULD SELL IT IN SUPERMARKETS AFTER MY COURT CASE WAS OVER. TIRED BUT WIRED, I SET OFF FOR A LITTLE JOB I HAD TO DO IN CONGLETON SQUARE. I LEFT AN HOUR JUST TO GET OFF THE ESTATE.

THE MAJORITY OF ARCHITECTS ARE DEDICATED ANARCHISTS. THEY HAD DESIGNED THE BLUEBIRD FARM ESTATE IN SUCH A WAY THAT VIOLENT SOCIAL UPHEAVAL WAS A CERTAINTY. MILES OF PISS-STAINED CORRIDORS, TUNNELS AND GANTRIES.

OVER THE YEARS THE BLUEBIRD FARM HAD COME TO RESEMBLE A BATTLEFIELD - SPECIFICALLY THE YPRES SALIENT IN THE SUMMER OF 1916.

ON REACHING GROUND LEVEL I ENTERED A NETWORK OF TRENCHES. OCASIONALLY I HAD TO GIVE WAY TO OUTWARD RAIDING PARTIES OR MEDICS BRINGING BACK THE WOUNDED FROM THE FRONT.

MY ROUTE PASSED A GROUP OF RASTAFARIANS COMPOSING WAR POETRY, A PLATOON OF SIKHS AND SKINHEADS UNLIMBERING A HOWITZER NEAR THE COMMUNITY CENTRE AND A COMPANY OF SAPPERS BEING ENTERTAINED BY MARIE LLOYD SINGING A JINGOISTIC SONG.

USING AN ABANDONED TUNNEL WHICH HAD BEEN DUG BY THE SAPPERS, I EMERGED INSIDE A PHOTO-ME BOOTH IN BLUEBIRD FARM UNDERGROUND STATION. I RODE THE TUBE TO CONGLETON SQUARE.

I CROSSED THE GARDENS IN THE CENTRE OF THE SQUARE. SOME UNEMPLOYED WERE BEGGING FOR FOOD. SILLY SODS, THEY DIDN'T KNOW THAT THERE ARE THOUSANDS OF PLACES IN LONDON WHERE YOU CAN GET AS MUCH FREE FOOD AND DRINK AS YOU WANT. THE CATCH IS, YOU MUSTN'T BE HUNGRY OR THIRSTY OR YOU WON'T GET IN. BEFORE THE INJUNCTION I USED TO GET INVITED TO ALL KINDS OF THESE FREEBIES - LAUNCH PARTIES FOR NEW KINDS OF CLUBS, NEW KINDS OF GRAVY, NEW KINDS OF LAUNCHES. I TURNED THEM ALL DOWN WITH DISDAIN. NOW THEY WOULD ONLY INVITE ME IF I DID A TURN. I HAD TO RANT FOR MY SUPPER.

GENERALLY PEOPLE DON'T REALISE HOW TOUGH WRITING STAND-UP COMEDY IS. PENNING YOUR BEST ONE-LINER IS EQUIVALENT TO WRITING "TESS OF THE D'URBERVILLES." GIVING BIRTH TO A GREAT CATCH-PHRASE IS THE EQUIVALENT OF WRITING, PRODUCING, DIRECTING AND CHOREOGRAPHING "ANNIE GET YOUR GUN" AND TOURING IN IT FOR EIGHT YEARS.

I STARED UP AT THE UNWANTED BISCUITS BUILDING. IN THE NEW AGE OF CONSERVATION THE BLOCK HAD BEEN DESIGNED BY ARCHITECTS RUSSEL TRACTION AND PARTNERS AS A CLASSIC GEORGIAN TERRACE. UNFORTUNATELY IT WAS SEVENTY-FIVE FLOORS HIGH AND A QUARTER OF A MILE LONG.

VARIOUS SNIVELLING GUT-BUCKETS TOOK ME UP TO THE LARGE CHAIRMAN'S ROOM. THERE WAS A STAGE AT ONE END. RELUCTANTLY I STEPPED ONTO IT. HONEST, I TRIED TO KEEP MY MOUTH IN CHECK, BUT...

HONEST, I TRIED TO STICK TO THE STUPID ACT, BUT MY LEGAL PROBLEMS JUST SEEMED TO POP OUT...

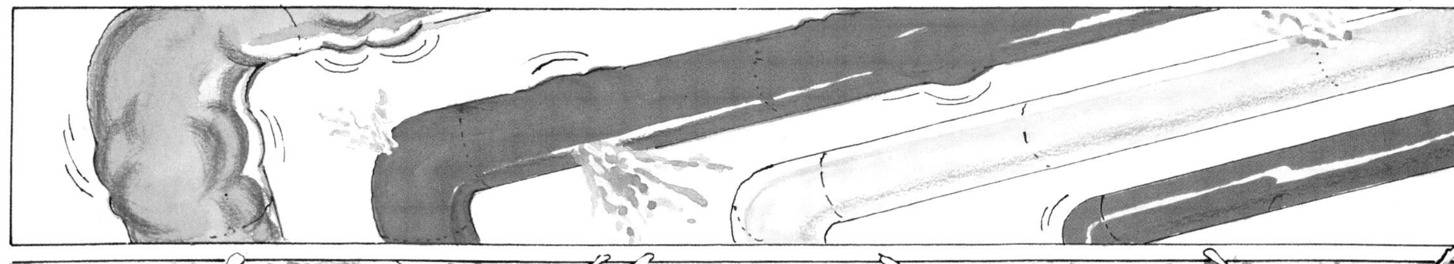

A COMEDIAN DYING IS A HORRIBLE THING. A COMEDIAN DYING IN A CONFINED SPACE IS A DOUBLY HORRIBLE THING.

THE AWFUL EMBARRASSMENT I CREATED INSTANTLY OVERLOADED THE PARANOIA-COLLECTORS. THE PIPES BURST, SPRAYING BOILING WATER ALL OVER THE BUILDING. THEY CHASED ME AS FAR AS THE TUBE STATION.

"Clackety-Clack" sang Geoffrey as he raced through the tunnel.

At the next station he'll pick up lots more nice people. Here we are. Here's a regular. A Very Important Person. Sir Jimmy MacTaggart!

Sir Jimmy was a Trade Unionist. He'd served his members so well he was now a Lord with a column in The "Daily Express". Sir Jimmy MacTaggart always wore his robes, even when he went down to the shops.
Ha, ha, silly Sir Jimmy.

At the next stop there were some more nice people and a nasty person. The Fat Comedian.

Geoffrey didn't like the Fat Comedian. He was nasty and he smelt a bit and Geoffrey was sure he hadn't paid the correct fare. The Fat Comedian sat down and sneered at Sir Jimmy.

Silly Fat Comedian. Sir Jimmy didn't notice. He wanted to go to the lavvy. He'd probably drunk too much lemonade at a picnic. He couldn't wait.

Look! There is a sign for a lavvy.

Funny. Didn't think they had them on tube trains. Oh well…

Sir Jimmy MacTaggart opened the door. Dark in here. never mind.

Zip.

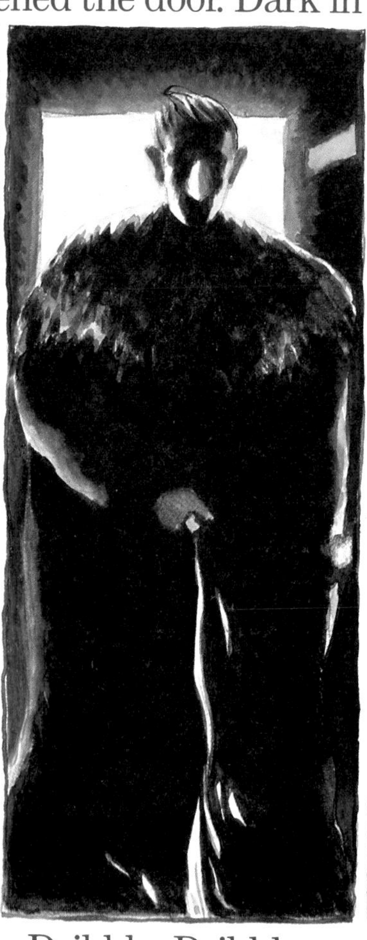

Dribble, Dribble.

Flash.

Bang!

Oh dear. This wasn't a lavvy. It was the rear driver's cab and there was a big hole in the floor. Sir Jimmy had gone to the lavvy on the live rail.

No more Sir Jimmy. What a way to go! Crikey!

IT WAS REALLY LATE WHEN I GOT HOME. THE TRANSPORT POLICE KEPT ALL THE PASSENGERS WHO'D WITNESSED THE INCINERATION OF SIR JIMMY MacTAGGART. I WAS GLAD THAT THE REACTIONARY OLD MOTHER-FUCKER WAS DEAD BUT THE SMELL OF FRYING ERMINE MADE ME FEEL A BIT ILL.

THE TRANSPORT POLICE ARE REALLY THICK - INDIVIDUALS WHO ARE TOO STUPID OR SADISTIC EVEN FOR THE REAL POLICE. MANY HAVE ACTUALLY FAILED THE INTELLIGENCE TEST FOR THE METROPOLITAN POLICE WHICH CONSISTS OF THE EXAMINEE FINDING THE CLOCKWORK MOUSE WHICH IS HIDDEN IN THE WENDY HOUSE, HUGGING AND KISSING IT AND GIVING IT A NICE NAME.

THEY THOUGHT THE HOLE IN THE FLOOR WAS A BIT ODD. I COULD HAVE SWORN THERE'D BEEN A SIGN SAYING "LAVATORY" ON THE DOOR BUT IT HAD VANISHED BY THE TIME THE POLICE GOT THERE SO I DIDN'T MENTION IT. THEY TOOK DOWN ALL OUR STATEMENTS WITH A STUMPY PENCIL INTO AN EXERCISE BOOK, THEN LET US GO.

ON THE WAY BACK TO MY FLAT I WAS NEARLY RUN OVER BY SOME JOY-RIDING SIX-YEAR-OLDS DRIVING A STOLEN TROIKA. JOY-RIDING WAS EPIDEMIC ON MOST ESTATES, BUT ON BLUEB THE KIDS HAD GOT TIRED OF RAZZING B.M.W AND JAGUARS AND HAD INSTEAD GONE FOR INTEREST AND VARIETY - RICKSHAWS, ROAD-ROLLERS AND J.C.B.s HURTLED ROUND THE ESTATE EVERY NIGHT.

I WAS TOO TIRED TO GO TO SLEEP. I DECIDED TO DO SOME WORK ON MY KIDDIES' BOOK. THERE SEEMED TO BE MORE PAGES THAN WHEN I LEFT. AH WELL, NEVER MIND.

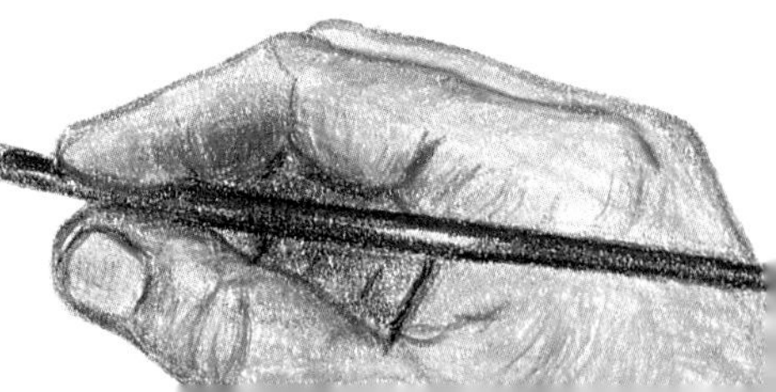

All the tube trains had finished work for the day. They went to bed at the big marshalling yard at Rum Junction. Rum Junction was a big yard.

All the express trains that went down to the coast used it too.
The express trains were very snobby. "We've got burger bars and toilets and two classes," they used to say.

But tonight they tried to earwig on the tube trains who were all too excited to sleep because none of them had ever had a murder on board before.

"Was it murder?" asked Robert, one of the trains.

"Yes, I think it was," said Geoffrey sadly.

"I'm afraid so, tube trains," said Driver Bob.

Now I know you're thinking, "Why hasn't Driver Bob gone home?" Well he didn't exactly have a home.

A while back Mrs Bob had fallen in love with Inspector Sid and chucked Driver Bob out. But every time Driver Bob managed to save up the deposit on a flat all the prices went up. So he lived in his cab. He'd made it very cosy. And anyway he liked tube trains better than people.

"Was it horrible?" asked a rather new and excitable tube train called Malcolm. "Was it gruesome? Was there Blood?" he thrilled. "Just calm down, young fellow," said Driver Bob.

"Yes, just calm down," said Geoffrey. But Malcolm was off. "Calm down! Calm down! You old trains are stupid, but I've got new headlights. I see things," he squawked.

"Pipe down," said the express train. "I won't," shouted Malcolm. "This city frightens me. I wish I was back up north, where I was made. This city is like a big weed gobbling up little towns as it keeps growing.

"Sometimes I think that down in the tunnels there's some brain that controls it all.
Yes, some evil entity living deep in the tubes.
It's there! It's there! I know it is!"

All the other tube trains had fallen silent, silent with sadness.
Sadness for the death of Sir Jimmy.
Sadness for themselves.
But mostly sadness because Malcolm was a fucking Loony.

T WAS MORNING WHEN I FINISHED DRAWING. I SLEPT ALL DAY. IN THE EVENING I PAID EXTRA CARE TO MY BEAUTY ROUTINE. I HAD AN IMPORTANT APPOINTMENT IN TANZANIA.

ALTHOUGH I COULDN'T WORK I HAD TO TRY AND KEEP MY CAREER BOILING. I WAS TRYING TO TOUC BASE WITH T.V. PEOPLE TO DO THE PREPARATORY WORK FOR MAYBE MY OWN SERIES, SO THAT ONCE THE INJUNCTION WAS LIFTED WE COULD START SHOOTING.

THAT NIGHT I HAD A MEET WITH CHANNEL FOUR'S HEAD OF YOUTH PROGRAMMES. HE WAS A NINE-YEAR-OLD BOY CALLED TIMMY COUSINS. WE'D ARRANGED TO MEET AT A COCKTAIL BAR CALLED TANZANIA IN PORKERS PARK.*

TANZANIA EBBED AND FLOWED ON THE TIDE OF FASHION, SOMETIMES IN, SOMETIMES OUT. WHEN I CAME IN IT WAS OUT, WHEN I WENT OUT IT WAS IN.

*FOOTNOTE. Porkers Park had once housed London's dung and fertiliser markets. Many fine buildings have been kept and renovated since the market moved. Gilbert Scott's Excrement Exchange is now a vegetarian restaurant and Inigo Jones's East India Guano Warehouse is now a dance studio. Tanzania was formerly the premises of T. E. Makepeace (Suppliers of Poo to the Gentry) and now housed a different kind of shit.

BECAUSE I WAS LATE THE KID HAD ALREADY DRUNK SEVERAL CHAMPAGNE AND VIMTO COCKTAILS AND WAS IN A BAD MOOD. I NEEDED TO BE ON TOP FORM.

LUCKILY I WAS. I TOLD MY FUNNY STORY ABOUT THE TROTSKYISTS AND THE CROCODILE, I DID MY FUNNY WALK AND SHOWED THE KID MY AMUSING SPOON.

I THINK HE WAS DIGGING WHERE I WAS COMING FROM.

THINGS WERE GOING SO WELL THAT HE SUGGESTED THAT I BUY HIM A MEAL IN A NEW LATE-NIGHT RESTAURANT SOUTH OF THE RIVER IN PAXTON. THE JOINT WAS CALLED "FRAZZLES"- IT WAS A CONVERTED ELECTRICITY SUB-STATION.

FUNNY EVERYTHING IN THIS TOWN USED TO BE SOMETHING ELSE. ALL THE OFFICES USED TO BE HOUSES, ALL THE SHITTY PLACES USED TO BE NICE PLACES AND I USED TO BE FAMOUS.

"HURRY UP," SAID TIMMY. "WE MIGHT MISS SOMETHING."

LUCKILY THERE WEREN'T ANY TAXIS FOR ME TO PAY FOR, SO I SUGGESTED WE WALK TO PORKERS PARK STATION TO GET THE TUBE. ON THE WAY TO THE TUBE STATION WE PASSED HUNDREDS OF PEOPLE SLEEPING IN CARDBOARD PACKING CRATES.* ONCE I WOULD HAVE PASSED THEM BY, BUT NOW THAT I WAS ONLY ONE STEP AWAY FROM MY HOME BEING A JAFFA BOX I FELT TREMENDOUS SYMPATHY AND RIGHTEOUS ANGER ON BEHALF OF THE HOMELESS. YOUNG TIMMY SAID "LOOK AT THOSE LAZY NORTHERN FUCKERS, WHY DON'T THEY GET A JOB IN TELEVISION AND STOP LITTERING THE STREETS." "FUCKING RIGHT," I SAID.

*FOOTNOTE. The housing situation in London is desperate. Ninety pounds a week is the going rate to live in the drip tray of somebody's fridge.

I PAID FOR THE TICKETS AND WE TOTTERED DOWN THE PLATFORM. SEEING AS THINGS WERE GOING SO WELL BETWEEN US I THOUGHT IT WAS THE RIGHT MOMENT TO PRESS THE KID.

HE SAID, "LET ME TELL YOU ABOUT THE FIVE STAGES OF BRITISH SHOW BIZ: ONE: *'WHO'S ALEXEI SAYLE?'* TWO: *'GET ME ALEXEI SAYLE.'* THREE: *'GET ME AN ALEXEI SAYLE TYPE WHO'S BEEN TO PUBLIC SCHOOL'.* FOUR: *'GET ME A YOUNG ALEXEI SAYLE TYPE WHO'S BEEN TO PUBLIC SCHOOL'.* FIVE: *'WHO'S ALEXEI SAYLE?'* WELL, WHO ARE YOU, FAT BOY?

Geoffrey had stopped on a Southern Line platform that was part of a mighty railway terminus. Somebody had pulled the communication cord. Naughty.

Stopped, going the other way, was Malcolm, the excitable new train. He was twitching a bit. “I’ve been asking around,” he whispered to Geoffrey, “And I reckon there’s been several killings on the Southern Line but they’ve been hushed up.”

“You want to stow that talk, young fellow,” hissed Geoffrey. “Who’d want to go around killing tube travellers?”

“Those people,” said Malcolm, indicating a group of admittedly geeky looking individuals hanging around at the end of the main line railway station.

"Why, they're just Train Spotters!" said Geoffrey.

"Are they? Are they?" said Malcolm. "They're always around. They see everything! Everything! I reckon they're the eyes and ears of the evil entity that lurks within these tunnels! I do! I do! I bet they're controlled by a man called Mr Gibson! Oh yes! Oh yes!"

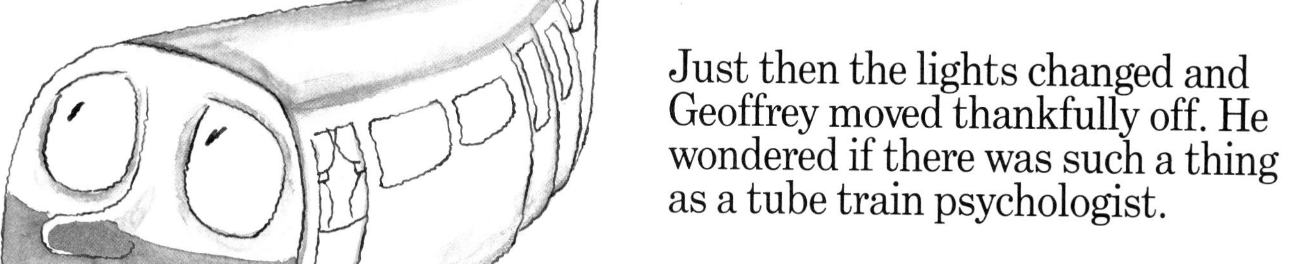

Just then the lights changed and Geoffrey moved thankfully off. He wondered if there was such a thing as a tube train psychologist.

As he came racketing into Porkers Park he could see into the station. Oh dear, there was the Fat Comedian again.
He was being shouted at by a young boy.

Geoffrey knew the young boy. He was a regular. Nice young boy.

Geoffrey raced into the station.

Suddenly the nice young boy was flying under Geoffrey's wheels.

Oh dear. Oh how the Fat Comedian screamed and screamed! Oh how the Fat Comedian ran and ran!

I RAN STRAIGHT INTO TWO TRANSPORT POLICE WHO'D BEEN FIGHTING OVER A TEDDY BEAR THEY'D FOUND IN A LITTER BIN. THEY ARRESTED ME AND TOOK ME TO THEIR UNDERGROUND POLICE STATION. AFTER BEING INTERROGATED FOR FIVE SECONDS I CONFESSED TO KILLING TIMMY COUSINS. I ALSO CONFESSED TO BEING A MEMBER OF BUCKS FIZZ AND TO ASSASSINATING ARCHDUKE FERDINAND OF YUGOSLAVIA.

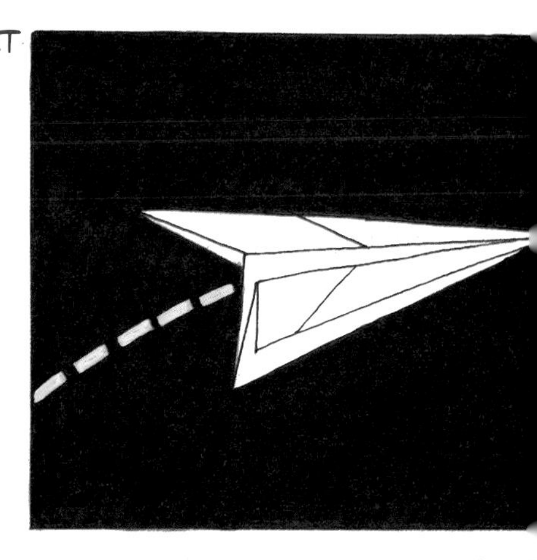

LUCKILY FOR ME THEY HAD TO LET ME GO. NOBODY ON THE PLATFORM WOULD BE A WITNESS. FOR ONCE THE TRADITIONAL GUTLESSNESS OF THE TUBE PASSENGER HAD HELPED SOMEONE. ONE TIME A TURK HAD SLAUGHTERED AND BUTCHERED AN OX DURING RUSH HOUR ON THE DISTRICT LINE AND NOT ONE OF THE TIMID PASSENGERS LET OUT A PEEP.

I WONDERED WHETHER LONDON TURNED ITS CITIZENS INTO JELLIES OR WHETHER IT WAS THE JELLIES WHO FLOURISHED.

AS I LEFT THE POLICE STATION I WAS APPROACHED BY A GEEKY-LOOKING GEEZER – ANORAK, CHEAP CAMERA AND WHAT I PRESUMED WAS HIS LUNCH IN A TUPPERWARE BOX. HE SPOKE TO ME. "MR SAYLE? I'M MR GIBSON." HE HAD ONE OF THOSE NUTTY-NORMAN VOICES THAT PEOPLE USE TO TELL YOU THAT THE CBI PUT WIRES IN THEIR HEADS OR THAT PRINCE CHARLES IS AN ASTRONAUT.

"LOOK, I HAVE A LITTLE PROPOSITION FOR YOU. THE TRANSPORT POLICE SUSPECT YOU OF THE MURDER OF SIR JIMMY AND YOUNG TIMMY COUSINS. NOW I KNOW YOU DIDN'T DO IT BUT THE ENTITY... I MEAN... ORGANISATION I WORK FOR WOULD LIKE TO FIND OUT WHO IS RESPONSIBLE. AFTER ALL, PEOPLE MUST NOT BE AFRAID TO TRAVEL ON THE TUBE. I CAN ALSO SAY THAT THERE HAVE BEEN OTHER KILLINGS ON THE SOUTHERN LINE. GOD KNOWS, YOU HAVE PLENTY OF FREE TIME, YOU WERE A POLICEMAN ONCE,* YOU NEED TO CLEAR YOURSELF FROM SUSPICION AND YOU SOLVED A MURDER ON A TRAIN ONCE.** PERFECT! NOW HERE'S A LIST OF THE PREVIOUS SUSPICIOUS DEATHS, A CORNISH PASTY AND A WEEK'S 'GO-ANYWHERE' RAIL PASS." "NOW HANG ON," I CRIED, BUT HE'D VANISHED.

*FOOTNOTE. See "Alexei Sayle and The Turtle that Sang Monteverdi" (An Inspector Alexei Sayle Mystery)

**FOOTNOTE. See "Train to Hell" (Another Fucking Alexei Sayle Mystery)

I GOT THE BUS HOME.

It was afternoon in Rum Junction. There were some train spotters hanging around waiting for an interesting coal train to come through. When they saw the interesting train they would write its number down in a book.

"What's the point of that?" Geoffrey asked Driver Bob.

"Well," said Driver Bob thoughtfully, "Essentially they're timid, fearful souls who by trying to catalogue and impose order on one…

…tiny tiny part of the universe are attempting to fend off the yawning void of terror at the heart of existence, the appalling blackness… the blackness … the terrible blackness…" Driver Bob stopped, gasping for breath.

"Steady on, old chap," said Geoffrey. "Sorry, old man," said Driver Bob. "Got a bit carried away there."

I DECIDED ON BREAKFAST. THEY MOVED TEN THOUSAND PEOPLE TO BLUEBIRD FARM AND FOR FIFTEEN YEARS THERE WERE NO SHOPS.
WHEN SOME WERE FINALLY BUILT THEY WERE TAKEN OVER BY THE PARASITIC SCUM WITH THE HIGHEST PROFIT MARGINS – BUILDING SOCIETIES AND ESTATE AGENTS.

I HATE ESTATE AGENTS MORE THAN I HATE FASCISM. EVERY SHOP IN EVERY HIGH STREET IS EITHER A BUILDING SOCIETY, A BANK OR AN ESTATE AGENT. LUCKILY SOME OF THE MORE ENTERPRISING EMPLOYEES HAD STARTED SELLING THE NECCESSITIES OF LIFE. I HAD A CAPUCCINO AND A BELGIAN BUN AT THE NOTTINGHAM AND BONKSHIRE AND MULLED OVER MY LATEST CASE.
I HAD NO CLUES AND NO SUSPECTS, BUT I HAD A POLICEMAN'S INSTINCTS, A POLICEMAN'S METHODS AND A POLICEMAN'S HAT –
A LITTLE PLASTIC ONE I'D BOUGHT IN OXFORD STREET.

THE OPPORTUNITY OF TRACKING DOWN THE SOUTHERN LINE KILLER SEEMED A MORE ENTICING PROSPECT THAN THE HOPELESS TASK OF TRYING TO REBUILD MY CAREER. I HAD ONE MORE APPOINTMENT THEN I WOULD BE FREE TO INVESTIGATE.
WITH RENEWED VIGOUR AND VIGILANCE I CAUGHT THE TUBE TO CHOOSEY CIRCUS, HEADED FOR THE PRONTO DISTRICT.

THE SHRIEKING NEON LIGHTS PROCLAIMED IT TO BE THE CENTRE OF SLEAZE AND SLIME, THE SHAMELESS FOUL'D WINDS OF PROSTITUTION BLEW STRONGEST HERE: IT WAS THE CENTRE OF THE ADVERTISING BUSINESS.

ON THE ENTERTAINMENT EVOLUTIONARY SCALE, ADVERTISING PEOPLE ARE THE LOWEST, THE PRIMEVA SLIME, THE MOST DESPICABLE, THE MOST DROOLINGEST SUB-HUMANEST. YOU KNOW THOSE THREE CHIMPS THAT DO THE TEA ADS - THEY'RE THE OWNERS OF THE AD AGENCY THAT'S GOT THE ACCOUNT.

IN THE OLD DAYS I HAD BEEN BESIEGED BY AD AGENCIES TO DO VOICEOVERS, FUNNY TV LAGER ADS AND EVEN TO ENDORSE AN ALEXEI SAYLE RANGE OF PRODUCTS - MR SWEARY DOLLS, MR FATBASTAR PORKY-PIE HATS, DR MARTEN'S JOGGING BOOTS. I TURNED THEM ALL DOWN BECAUSE I SAID I HAD PRINCIPLES.

SINCE THE INJUNCTION I'D BEGGED THE AGENCIES TO GIVE ME ANYTHING AT ALL. FINALLY SOMEBODY AT GIBLET, GOB & MICKEY SAID THEY'D MAYBE GIVE ME A TEST FOR A RADIO VOICE OVER. IF SHOWBIZ IS A JUNGLE THEN ADVERTISING IS A SWAMP, OFTEN LITERALLY. FOLLOWING THE FASHION TO HAVE ATRIUMS - SMALL FORESTS - AS THE CENTREPIECE OF OFFICE BLOCKS, THE GGM BUILDING WAS A SIZEABLE SLICE OF PUNGENT FOETID CREEPER-HUNG ORINOCO SLIME.

MY CONTACT - GERRY GIBLET - LIVED UNDER A STONE NEAR THE ENTRANCE. I COULD SEE HIS NASTY EYES PEEPING AT ME. HE SLID OUT TO MEET ME. WHEN HE SPOKE HIS WORDS SEEMED TO BE A REPTILIAN SLITHER. "AAAALLEXEE, TREMENDOUS HARD LUCK AAABOUT THE LITIGATION. NEVER MIND, COME THIS WWWWAY, MAATE."

WE SWUNG FROM VINE TO VINE UP TO THE LITTLE DUBBING STUDIO CONTAINED IN A TREE HOUSE.

THERE WAS SOMETHING ABOUT BEING SHUT IN A GLASS BOX WITH THIS LIZARD. I HAD BEEN TRYING TO GET MY OLD LIFE BACK AGAIN BUT SOMEHOW IT DIDN'T SEEM SO DESIRABLE ANYMORE.

GERRY PRATTLED ON. "SURE, SURE," I SAID, AND "ABSOLUTELY RIGHT, SMASHING." BUT IN MY MIND WAS RUNNING A PARALLEL RANT THAT WENT, "GO FUCK YOURSELF, YOU PRICK," AND: "STUFF IT, SLIMEBALL."

GERRY SAID "THIS VOICEOVER IS FOR A NEW TEA-TIME SNACK FOR DOGS. NOW THIS WORD HERE *'WHEATY'* - IF YOU COULD PRONOUNCE THAT WITH A SENSE OF INEFFABLE LONGING. BUT *'CRUNCH'* SHOULD PERHAPS EVOKE A DISTANT VISTA OF AMBER WAVES OF GRAIN STRETCHING TOWARDS A LIMITLESS HORIZON WITH PERHAPS A SMUDGE OF SMOKE IN THE LEFT HAND CORNER AND COULD YOU DO IT IN ONE-AND-A-HALF SECONDS."*

"NO PROBLEMS, FUCK PANTS," I SAID, MY MIND BEGINNING TO SEEP INTO MY MOUTH.

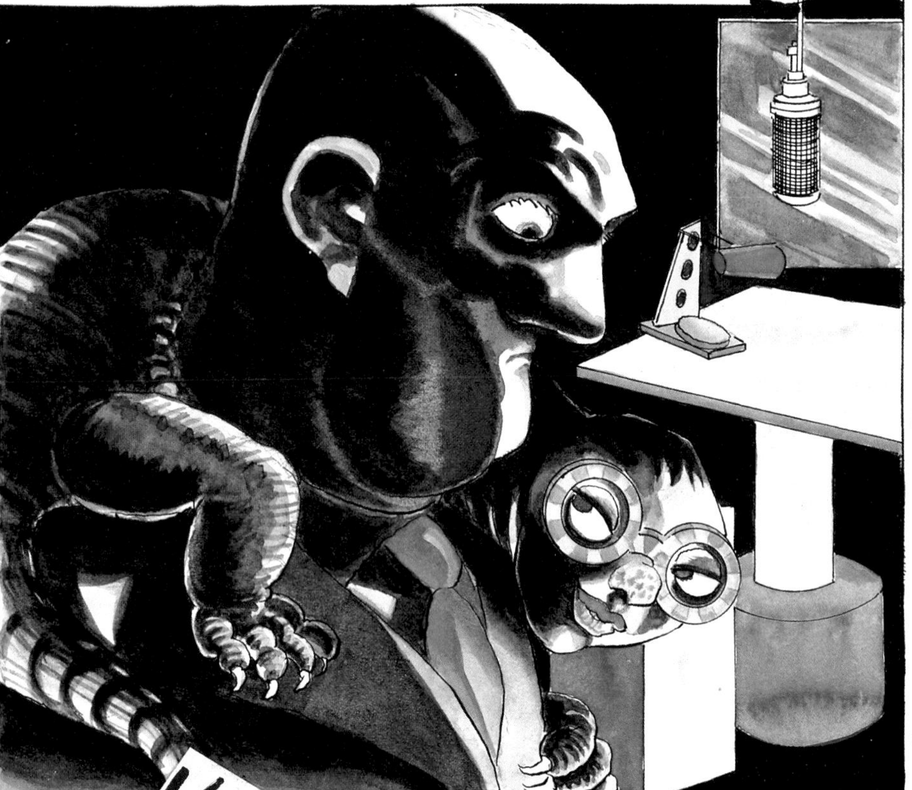

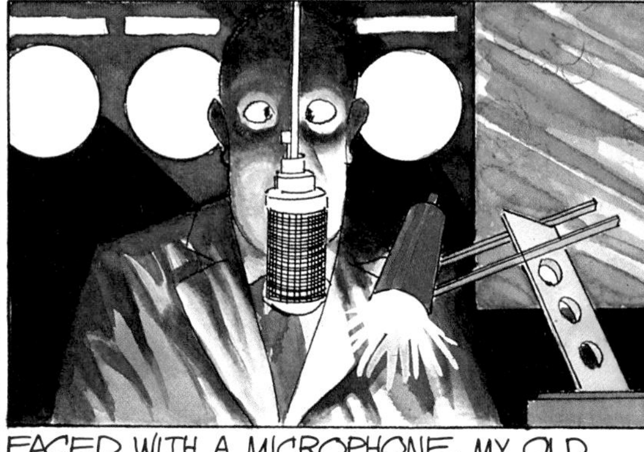

FACED WITH A MICROPHONE, MY OLD PROBLEM RETURNED.

*FOOTNOTE. Douglas Fairbanks once did some job or other lasting maybe half an hour and got fifty thousand dollars and some envious bystander said "Fifty thousand dollars for half an hour's work, Jeez!" And Fairbanks, hearing him, said, "Not half an hour's work dear boy - a lifetime's." The lying old fuck, the hypocritical old gobshite - of course it was for half an hour's work.

was early morning. Geoffrey the tube
ain and Driver Bob rumbled through
e marshalling yards at North Cake.
Iappy happy happy," said Bob as he
ove. "Jolly jolly jolly," said Geoffrey
he rolled along.
"There's something weird
about those two," said
Arnold the shunting
engine.
"Well, said Sammy the signal box,
"It's a problem of anthropo-
orphism, isn't it? Being a character
a children's book and an inanimate
object can tend to make one two-
dimensional."
"Bloody nonsense," said Marcia the
piece of gravel. "I'm amazingly
complex."
"Yeah, me too,"
said Gilbert the
fence post.
"Can you keep the
fucking noise down,"
said Terry the tuft of
grass. "Some of us
objects are trying to
sleep."

EARLY THE NEXT MORNING I CAUGHT THE FIRST TRAIN GOING NORTH HEADING FOR RIDGELEY HALT. AT RUBBERY PARK WE EMERGED INTO DAYLIGHT. I WAS ASTONISHED TO SEE FARMLAND ON EITHER SIDE OF THE TRACKS. WE ENTERED THE LITTLE-USED TEASMAID LANE LOOP.
AT TALL FARM I GOT OFF.

I WAS AMAZED TO BE STANDING ON THE PLATFORM OF A PRETTY COUNTRY STATION WITH FARMLAND STRETCHING TO THE HORIZON.
FARMLAND SO NEAR LONDON SEEMED A BIZARRE CONFLUENCE. I FELT A BIT EDGY. I'VE NEVER LIKED THE COUNTRY. IT HASN'T GOT A ROOF ON IT AND, I DON'T CARE WHAT PEOPLE SAY ABOUT SHEEP, I THINK THEY HAVE A KNOWING SARCASTIC LOOK IN THEIR EYES AS IF, ONE DAY, AT A GIVEN SIGNAL, THEY'LL ALL TURN NASTY LIKE IN "THE BIRDS," CHAMPING AT PEOPLE WITH THEIR BIG YELLOW TEETH.

TOO NERVOUS TO LEAVE THE STATION I HOVERED ON THE PLATFORM, WAITING FOR THE NEXT TRAIN. FURTHER DOWN THE PLATFORM SAT A SHABBY INDIVIDUAL WHO SEEMED TO BE LOOKING AT ME. I REMEMBERED HE HAD BEEN ON THE TRAIN UP AND HAD BEEN WATCHING ME THEN. AT THE TIME I ASSUMED FROM HIS UNKEMPT APPEARANCE AND TWITCHY, NERVOUS MANNER THAT HE WAS ONE OF MY FEW REMAINING FANS. BUT NOW I WASN'T SURE.

MY FIRST STEP TOWARDS HIM SENT HIM SCUTTLING DOWN THE PLATFORM. A FEW MORE STEPS AND HE BOLTED ONTO THE FORBIDDEN ZONE OF THE RAILWAY TRACK.

HESITATING ONLY FOR A SPLIT SECOND I PELTED AFTER HIM. NECK AND NECK WE TURNED INTO A SMALL MARSHALLING YARD. FEELING MY BREATH GOING I FLUNG MYSELF AT HIM. LIKE A JET-PROPELLED ZEPPELIN I SQUELCHED HIM TO THE GROUND. I LAY GASPING ON TOP OF HIM HALF IN, HALF OUT OF THE UNKEMPT UNDERGROWTH AT THE EDGE OF THE YARD. VERY CLOSE I COULD HEAR THE ROAR OF A MIGHTY MOTORWAY JUNCTION. THE THICK UNDERGROWTH FORMED BOTH THE RAILWAY BANK AND THE VERGE OF THE MOTORWAY.

SEEING AS THE MAN WAS SMALLER AND WEAKER THAN ME, I DECIDED TO KNOCK HIM ABOUT A BIT.

"WHO ARE YOU?" I SHOUTED. "DID YOU KILL SIR JIMMY MacTAGGART AND YOUNG TIMMY COUSINS?"
"GARRKH," HE CROAKED. I LET GO OF HIS TONGUE. "COME TO THINK OF IT, I'VE SEEN RATHER A LOT OF PEOPLE LIKE YOU SINCE I'VE BEEN RIDING THE TUBE."
"I DIDN'T KILL ANYBODY MISTER," HE SAID. "I'M JUST A LATE COMMUTER." "A WHAT?" I SAID.

A LATE COMMUTER. YOU SEE US ALL THE TIME, TOWARDS THE END OF THE MORNING RUSH HOUR, LATE AGAIN, INCAPABLE OF GETTING UP IN TIME, STILL IN OUR PYJAMAS, FLINGING OURSELVES AT THE CLOSING DOORS, KNOWING IF WE'RE LATE ONCE MORE IT'S THE SACK. EVENTUALLY WE DO LOSE OUR JOBS, THEN WE JUST RIDE THE RAILS, AIMLESS, WE BAND TOGETHER AND MAKE SOME KIND OF A LIFE DOWN THERE IN THE TUBE.

IT'S US WHO JAM UP THE CHOCOLATE MACHINES TO STEAL THE COINS. IT'S US WHO HIDE IN THE BACK OF PHOTO-ME BOOTHS AND TAKE YOUR CASH, RETURNING NOTHING EXCEPT FROM TIME TO TIME A BLURRED PHOTO OF A SAD AND DISPIRITED STRANGER. WE'RE TOO TIMID TO KILL THOSE PEOPLE. BUT ALL THIS ATTENTION IS NOT GOOD FOR US SO I'VE BEEN FOLLOWING YOU, TRYING TO PLUCK UP COURAGE TO TELL YOU WHO DID...

I IMMEDIATELY GUESSED WHAT HAD HAPPENED. IT IS A WELL KNOWN FACT THAT WHILE THE REST OF THE COUNTRYSIDE HAS BEEN TURNED INTO A DUSTBOWL BY CHEMICAL FARMING, WHERE NO BIRD TWEETS OR ANIMAL GROWLS, BY CONTRAST, THE NEGLECTED VERGES OF MOTORWAYS, MAJOR ROADS AND RAILWAY EMBANKMENTS HAVE BECOME HAVENS FOR THE SPECIES OF FLORA AND FAUNA THAT HAVE LONG BECOME EXTINCT IN THE REST OF THE COUNTRYSIDE.

THE LATE COMMUTER WAS MY ONLY CLUE, SO, HESITATING BRIEFLY, I PLUNGED INTO THE LONG GRASS AND RARE PLANTS AT THE EDGE OF THE YARD. IT WAS THUS THAT I ENTERED *THE RAILWAY EMBANKMENT THAT TIME FORGOT.*

SOON THE HUM OF THE TRAFFIC FADED AND WAS REPLACED WITH THE STRANGE JUNGLE CRIES OF SMALL SLITHERY THINGS BEING KILLED BY FAT FURRY THINGS AND BIG SCALY THINGS CRUSHING LITTLE SPIKY WET THINGS.

THE SKY DARKENED AS THE LUSH VEGETATION FORMED A GLOOMY CEILING. AGAINST THE ODD GLIMPSE OF BLUE PTERODACTYLS WHEELED, THEIR MIGHTY BONE-CRUSHING BEAKS SWIVELLING FROM SIDE TO SIDE.

AFTER HALF AN HOUR OF HACKING THROUGH DENSE FOREST I SLICED THROUGH A LIANA VINE AND STUMBLED ONTO A COBBLED ROAD. AN OLD FASHIONED WOODEN ROADSIGN POINTED UP THE ROAD. IT SAID "WIDDICOMBE - UNDER-MOPED 1 MILE." KEEPING TO THE SIDE OF THE ROAD I TOPPED A RISE AND THERE, SPREAD OUT BELOW IN A MIST-TINGED HOLLOW, WAS THE MOST DELIGHTFUL LITTLE TOWN I HAD EVER SEEN.

I WAS SO ENGROSSED THAT I WAS TERRIFIED BY A SUDDEN HONK AND CLATTER BEHIND ME. IN A CLOUD OF PETROL AND OIL A MAN RATTLED PAST ME ON A MOTORBIKE – AND WHAT A BIKE – IT WAS A LONG TIME SINCE I'D SEEN A 1200 c.c. VINCENT, THE FINEST ENGLISH BIKE EVER MADE. STRANGER STILL, AS HE WAVED CHEERILY AND HEADED INTO TOWN I NOTICED HE WASN'T WEARING A CRASH HELMET.

IN A STATE OF WONDERMENT I ENTERED THE TOWN. THERE WEREN'T MANY CARS ABOUT AND THOSE THERE WERE WERE *ROVERS, STANDARD TRIUMPHS, HUMBERS, ARMSTRONG-SIDDELEY SAPPHIRES* – NOT A NISSAN IN SIGHT. ALL THE BUILDINGS WERE NEAT AND TIDY EXCEPT FOR ONE – A DERELICT STATION. THE RUSTED SIGN READ *"SOUTHERN LINE – WIDDICOMBE – UNDER-MOPED"* AND PASTED OVER IT READ *"CLOSED JUNE 1964."* I WENT INTO THE PUB.

IT HAD A PUBLIC BAR, A SALOON, A FOUR-ALE BAR AND A SNUG. I STARED IN AWE AT THE LUNCHTIME MENU - BRAISED OXTAIL, THREE VEG AND COLLEGE PUDDING - ONE AND SIXPENCE. STEAK AND KIDNEY PUDDING BUBBLE AND SQUEAK AND TREACLE PUDDING - ONE AND NINE. A PINT OF BITTER WAS A SHILLING. "HELLO THERE," SAID THE LANDLORD. "WE DON'T GET MANY VISITORS HERE."

"HOW CAME TO BE THIS PLACE?" I SAID. I NOTICED I HAD STARTED TO TALK AS IF I WAS IN AN EARLY VERSION OF *'LOST HORIZON'*. "WELL," HE SAID, "WHEN THE MOTORWAY WAS BUILT AND THE STATION CLOSED DOWN WE BECAME CUT OFF. WE NEVER LIKED THE MODERN WORLD, EVEN IN 1964, SO WE DECIDED TO STAY CUT OFF. HERE A NEW SUIT COSTS TEN GUINEAS, THERE'S NO HIDEOUS MODERN ARCHITECTURE AND *'FOUR FEATHER FALLS'* IS STILL ON THE TELLY."
I COULD HARDLY BELIEVE MY EARS. I HAD ALWAYS DREAMT OF SUCH A PLACE - UNTAINTED BY THE STINK OF MODERNISM IN ALL ITS FORMS.
THE LANDLORD WENT ON.

THINKING QUICKLY, I CLIMBED ONTO A CHAIR. I KNEW I HAD TO MAKE THE SPEECH OF MY LIFE.

Geoffrey and Driver Bob were doing the first southbound train that day. They chatted as they left Ridgeley Halt.

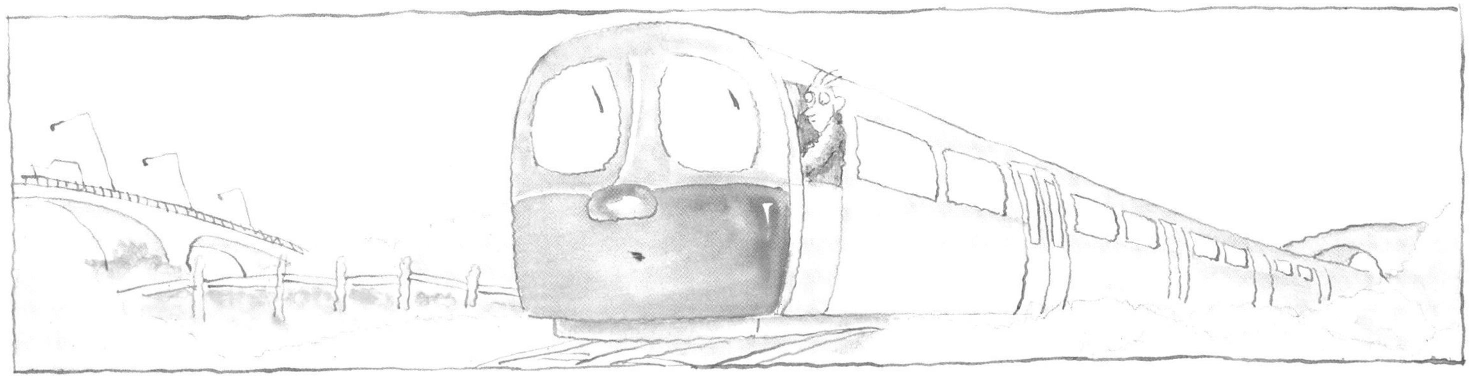

"Was your divorce very traumatic, Bob?" asked Geoffrey. "Yes," said Driver Bob. "It was a very messy divorce. The judge ate egg mayonnaise sandwiches all through the proceedings and they dribbled everywhere."

"But you've got me now, Bob," said Geoffrey.
"Yes," said Driver Bob. "I think of you as the brother I never wanted."

"We never pick up any passengers on the first train any more," said Geoffrey.

"No. We used to be full of factory workers, decent people who made things, but that's all gone. There's only the parasite office workers and they don't get up until nine," replied Driver Bob.

"Still, there's a few less of the parasites," giggled Geoffrey. "Tee, hee," tittered Driver Bob.

"Didn't we laugh when we fried Sir Jimmy?" said Geoffrey.

"Yeah, and wasn't it good when I pushed that horrible kid onto the track. That was brilliant. One less T.V. cunt," said Driver Bob.*

*FOOTNOTE. Murder One – Driver Bob made the hole in the floor and knowing that Sir Jimmy would be drunk and needing a lavvy, stuck the sign up. He took it down again after Sir Jimmy was fried.

Murder Two – While the emergency handle was pulled, Driver Bob ran along the tunnel to Porkers Park. Geoffrey drove himself into the station and Bob pushed Timmy Cousins under his wheels.

WHEN I CAME TO I WAS BACK IN THE JUNGLE AT THE EDGE OF THE MARSHALLING YARD. NEXT TO ME WAS THE RAVAGED BODY OF THE LATE COMMUTER.

MUTTERING TO MYSELF, "BASTARDS, WANKERS," I LIMPED BACK TO THE STATION. IT WAS DUSK. I SAT DOWN AND WAITED FOR A TRAIN. I CLIMBED ABOARD WHEN IT ARRIVED AND SLUMPED INTO A SEAT.

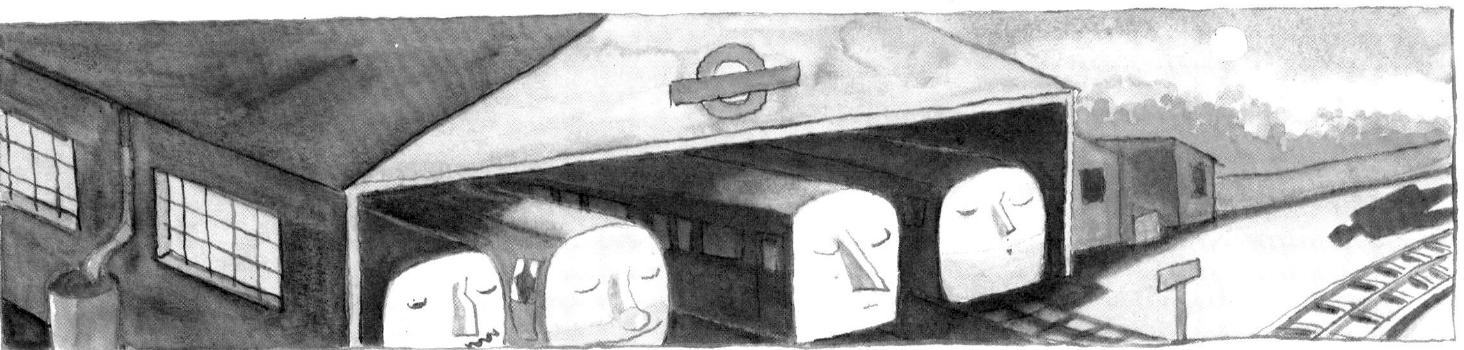

It was late at night in Rum Junction. All the tube trains were asleep. The only sound was the soft hiss of hydraulics.

Geoffrey felt a pebble klonk against the windscreen. He flicked on his headlights. In their blaze was the Fat Comedian.

"Sod off, Fatty," said Driver Bob in a menacing voice.

I FELT A FOOL STANDING THERE. IT WAS THE MIDDLE OF THE NIGHT AND I WAS TALKING TO A TUBE TRAIN. BUT IT WAS THE ONLY WAY OUT FOR ALL THREE OF US. "YOU'RE GOING TO GET CAUGHT IF YOU GO ON TOPPING THE PASSENGERS FOR MUCH LONGER," I SAID.
"NOW, I CAN UNDERSTAND WHY YOU DO IT, HAVING TO PRETEND TO BE JOLLY, JOLLY, JOLLY ALL DAY LONG WITH ALL THOSE BASTARDS, SHITBAGS, WANKERS GETTING ON AND OFF. BUT YOU KNOW, THERE IS A WAY OUT." TAKING OUT A COCONUT, A PENCIL AND A PEELED PRAWN I ILLUSTRATED WHAT I HAD TO SA

TO KEEP THIS SOCIETY, CAPITALIST SOCIETY, GOING, PEOPLE MUST BE PERSUADED TO BUY MORE AND MORE THINGS. TO DO THAT THEY MUST BE CONVINCED THAT TRUE HAPPINESS AND FULFILMENT LIES IN BUYING MORE AND MORE AND BETTER AND BETTER THINGS. BUT WHEN THEY GET THESE THINGS THERE IS NO HAPPINESS SO THEY FRANTICALLY TRY TO GET MORE THINGS. NOW THAT HARD TIMES ARE HERE LONDON HAS SUCKED ALL THE THINGS FROM THE REST OF THE COUNTRY.
HERE IN LONDON, PEOPLE ARE STUFFED WITH THINGS AND LONDON IS STUFFED WITH THINGS TO BE TAKEN AND PEOPLE IN LONDON ARE PREPARED TO DO TERRIBLE THINGS TO GET THE MONEY TO BUY MORE THINGS. THAT'S WHY THIS TOWN IS SO FULL OF FIXERS, MANAGERS, SHARPIES, WANKERS, CUNTS AND PRICKS.
BUT IF IT'S LIKE THAT HERE, THEN IT ISN'T LIKE HERE ANYWHERE ELSE. WE NEED TO GO SOMEWHERE WHERE PEOPLE DON'T HAVE THINGS. WE COULD GO UP NORTH TOGETHER OR THE MIDLANDS. YOU COULD FIND SOME CLAPPED-OUT OLD METRO SYSTEM. I'M NOT SAYING IT'S PARADISE UP THERE. PEOPLE CAN BE AWFUL, BUT I RECKON THEY ARE NOT WANKERS THE WAY THEY ARE IN LONDON.

IT TOOK ME ALL AFTERNOON TO FIND HIM, CROSSING OFF ALL THE PLACES IN THE LISTINGS MAGAZINES AS I WENT. HE WAS AT A 'SEASON OF UNFUNNY OLD FILMS' AT THE NATIONAL FILM THEATRE.

THERE HE SAT IN THE PUZZLED DARK. MR SAUNDERS. ALL HIS WORKING LIFE MR SAUNDERS HAD BEEN INTO COMEDY. HE PRODUCED COMEDY RECORDS, MANAGED COMEDIANS, PRODUCED CHARITY COMEDY GALAS AND YET WAS TOTALLY WITHOUT A SENSE OF HUMOUR. SO WHY WAS HE SO OBSESSED WITH COMEDY? AFTER A COUPLE OF YEARS I FIGURED OUT THAT FOR THE NORMALLY HUMOROUS, HUMOUR IS A KIND OF CODE; A SINGLE WORD OR GESTURE CAN CRACK-UP A GROUP OF FRIENDS, BUT TO THE HUMOURLESS, LAUGHTER SEEMS TO BREAK OUT AT RANDOM ALL AROUND THEM AND THAT IS WHY THEY BECOME INVOLVED IN COMEDY – TO TRY AND CRACK THE CODE.

HE SCUTTLED AFTER ME AS I LED HIM ALONG THE EMBANKMENT. I LED HIM TO THE SOUTHERN LINE STATION AT SOUTH FISH. WE WENT DOWN INTO THE TUNNELS.

"NEARLY THERE," I SAID. "NEARLY THERE." BENEATH OUR FEET A RUMBLING BEGAN. "THERE'S A TRAIN COMING!" WE FLED DOWN PASSAGES AND CORRIDORS.

THE TRAIN WAITED WITH ITS DOORS OPEN. SPRINTING AHEAD I JUMPED ABOARD AS MR SAUNDERS FLUNG HIMSELF AT T OPENING. GEOFFREY SHUT HIS DOORS. MR SAUNDERS' HEAD WAS TRAPPED. RED CHANGED TO GREEN AND WE MOVED

ATLANTA

Programme of Events

The Centennial Olympic Games will be opened on Friday, July 19, 1996, in the new Olympic Stadium at Atlanta by the President of the United States. The Opening Ceremony will include the traditional rituals and the teams will march in, each led by their flag-bearer. The order for the nations remains consistent, with Greece always parading first, the host country last and the rest in alphabetical order in between. This is then followed by the entertainment, which in 1996 will focus on three themes – the Centennial of the Olympic Games, the American South and youth.

Tickets for the opening and, less formal, closing ceremonies are the most expensive and the most sought after of the Games. Both ceremonies take place in the Olympic Stadium and they are expected to draw a worldwide television audience of more than 3.5 billion people.

Competition begins on Saturday, July 20, in 11 sports, and finishes on Sunday, August 4, with the finals of eight sports and the closing ceremony.

FLYING THE FLAG As at Seoul in 1984, the Opening Ceremony will be a mass of action and colour

PROGRAMME OF EVENTS

SPORT	VENUE	JULY													AUGUST			
		19	20	21	22	23	24	25	26	27	28	29	30	31	1	2	3	4
		F	S	S	M	T	W	T	F	S	S	M	T	W	T	F	S	S
OPENING CEREMONY	OLYMPIC STADIUM	●																
AQUATICS: DIVING	GEORGIA TECH AQUATIC CENTER								●	●	●	●	●	●	●	●		
SWIMMING	GEORGIA TECH AQUATIC CENTER		●	●	●	●	●	●	●									
SYNCHRO	GEORGIA TECH AQUATIC CENTER												●			●		
WATER POLO	GEORGIA TECH AQUATIC CENTER		●	●	●	●	●		●	●	●							
ARCHERY	STONE MOUNTAIN PARK										●[1]	●	●	●	●	●		
ATHLETICS	OLYMPIC STADIUM								●	●	●	●		●	●	●	●	●
MARATHON	ATLANTA										●							●
RACE WALK	SUMMERHILL/GRANT PARK								●							●		
BADMINTON	GEORGIA STATE UNIVERSITY						●	●	●	●	●	●	●	●	●			
BASEBALL	ATLANTA-FULTON COUNTY STADIUM		●	●	●	●	●	●		●	●	●	●		●	●		
BASKETBALL	GEORGIA DOME/MOREHOUSE COLLEGE		●	●	●	●	●	●	●	●	●	●	●	●	●	●	●	●
BOXING	ALEXANDER MEMORIAL COLISEUM		●	●	●	●	●	●	●	●	●		●	●	●	●	●	●
CANOEING: SLALOM	OCOEE WHITEWATER CENTER, TENN								●[2]	●	●							
SPRINT	LAKE LANIER												●	●	●	●	●	●
CYCLING: ROAD	ATLANTA			●										●				●
MOUNTAIN BIKING	GEORGIA INTERNATIONAL HORSE PARK												●					
TRACK	STONE MOUNTAIN PARK						●	●	●	●	●							
EQUESTRIAN SPORTS	GEORGIA INTERNATIONAL HORSE PARK			●	●	●	●	●[1]	●	●	●	●		●	●	●	●	
FENCING	GEORGIA WORLD CONGRESS CENTER		●	●	●	●	●	●										
FOOTBALL: PRELIMS	ORLANDO, FLA/WASHINGTON D.C.		●	●	●	●	●	●										
PRELIMS/Q-FINALS	BIRMINGHAM, ALA/MIAMI, FLA		●	●	●	●	●	●		●	●							
S-FINALS/FINALS	SANFORD STADIUM, ATHENS, GA										●			●	●	●	●	
GYMNASTICS: ARTISTIC	GEORGIA DOME		●	●	●	●	●	●			●	●	●[3]					
RHYTHMIC	UNIVERSITY OF GEORGIA														●	●	●	●
HANDBALL	GA WORLD CONGRESS CENTER/DOME						●	●	●	●	●	●	●	●	●	●	●	●
HOCKEY	M.BROWN COLL/CLARK ATLANTA UNIV		●	●	●	●	●	●	●	●	●	●	●	●	●	●		
JUDO	GEORGIA WORLD CONGRESS CENTER		●	●	●	●	●	●	●									
MODERN PENTATHLON	MULTIPLE SITES												●					
ROWING	LAKE LANIER			●	●	●	●	●	●	●	●							
SHOOTING	WOLF CREEK SHOOTING COMPLEX		●	●	●	●	●	●	●	●								
SOFTBALL	GOLDEN PARK, COLUMBUS			●	●	●	●	●	●	●		●	●					
TABLE TENNIS	GEORGIA WORLD CONGRESS CENTER					●	●	●	●	●	●	●	●	●	●			
TENNIS	STONE MOUNTAIN PARK					●	●	●	●	●	●	●	●	●	●	●	●	
VOLLEYBALL: BEACH	ATLANTA BEACH					●	●	●	●	●	●							
INDOOR	OMNI COLISEUM/UNIV OF GEORGIA		●	●	●	●	●	●	●	●	●	●	●	●	●	●	●	●
WEIGHTLIFTING	GEORGIA WORLD CONGRESS CENTER		●	●	●	●	●		●	●	●	●	●					
WRESTLING	GEORGIA WORLD CONGRESS CENTER		●	●	●	●							●	●	●	●		
YACHTING	WASSAW SOUND, SAVANNAH				●	●	●	●	●	●	●	●	●	●	●			
CLOSING CEREMONY	OLYMPIC STADIUM																	●

1 = NO SPECTATORS. 2 = TICKETED TRAINING. 3 = GALA EVENT.

THE EVENTS OF THE OLYMPIC GAMES

Apart from the first modern Olympics in 1896, in which there were nine sports, the number has varied between 14 and 20 plus. In Barcelona, in 1992, if the so-called "aquatic sports" were counted as four separate sports (swimming, diving, water polo and synchro), there were 28 sports in all, plus three demonstration sports.

How to satisfy the demand to expand the range of Olympic sports without making the Games impossibly unwieldy is a constant dilemma for the IOC. One sport, women's softball, has been added to the schedule for the Atlanta Games, and there will be no demonstration sports. Two more sports – triathlon and taekwondo – in Sydney in 2000, and sports such as ballroom dancing and bridge have been recognized by the IOC and may apply for acceptance.

Women's sports expand

Women's football makes its Olympic début in Atlanta, and women's basketball and volleyball have both had the number of teams competing increased from eight to 12. Other sports where women's participation has been substantially increased are cycling and fencing. Major disciplines to be introduced in Atlanta for both men and women are mountain-bike racing – replacing cycling's men-only team time trial – and beach volleyball. There are a few deletions, the most substantial being the compression of the modern pentathlon from four days to one, with the team event dropped.

The net result of all this is bound to increase the number of competitors in the Games. The official figure for the number expected in Atlanta is estimated to be just below 10,800, compared with the 9,364 who competed in Barcelona four years ago, with the proportion of women competitors rising from 29 percent to 36 percent.

Qualification

In team sports – including track and pool relay races – only one entry per country is permitted, and the Olympic programme is scheduled to accommodate a specific number of teams. A prequalifying competition takes place, usually in the form of regional tournaments, to reduce the number of entrants for participation in the Olympics proper.

For largely individual sports, such as athletics and swimming, to keep the entrants to a manageable number, countries may enter a maximum of three competitors provided they achieve, in a specified period before the Olympics, a standard time or distance laid down by their international federation. However, any IOC-affiliated country may enter one competitor in an event, whether or not that competitor has achieved the standard.

Some sports are limited to two competitors per country, while in others, such as boxing, it is one.

Prospecting for Gold

There are relatively few events that do not require the competitors to undergo further elimination competitions at the Games in order to reach a final. Heats are used in most racing events, while in sports such as boxing and tennis there is a straight knock-out tournament.

Another system, used in football for example, is to produce quarter- or semi-finalists from a number of round-robin groups. One-off events include the marathons and the cycling road races.

The Tenth Paralympic Games

On August 16, 12 days after the close of the Centennial Olympic Games of 1996, Atlanta will celebrate the opening of another anniversary Games, those of the tenth Paralympiad. The first international games for the handicapped were held at the Stoke Mandeville hospital, in England, where paralysed victims of the Second World War were treated. These developed into a world-wide movement, and every fourth year since 1960 the Paralympic Games have been held, whenever possible, in the country hosting the Olympic Games.

Using mostly the same venues as the Atlanta Olympics, some 3,500 athletes will take part in the tenth Paralympics, from 115 nations. They will compete in 17 medal sports (15 of which are Olympic sports) and two demonstration sports over a period of 10 days. At these Games, roughly one-third of the size of the Olympics, there will also be 1,000 coaches and team staff, 1,500 officials and technical personnel and 15,000 volunteers.

The Paralympics include events for competitors in wheelchairs, for amputees, for the blind or partially sighted and for those with cerebral palsy, and the sports will include archery, athletics, basketball, fencing, judo, swimming, tennis, volleyball and weightlifting.

At the Barcelona Paralympics in 1992, 23-year-old Tanni Grey (GBR) won four wheelchair track gold medals (100m, 200m, 400m and 800m), but she would be the first to say that the Paralympics is not just about winning. It is a demonstration of the "Triumph of the Human Spirit".

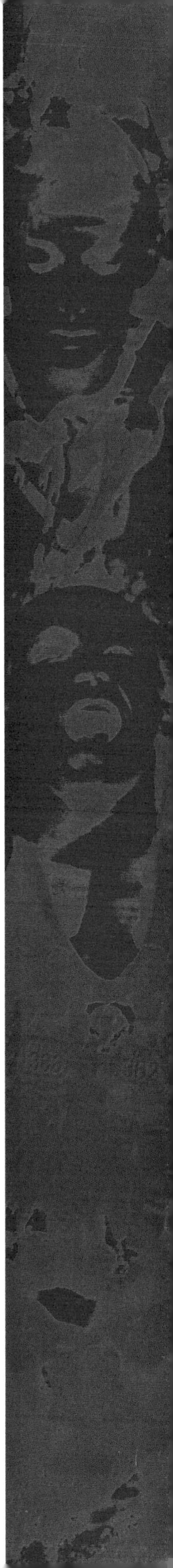

MOUNTAIN BIKING (LEFT): This exciting addition to the Games will be held at the equestrian park

BEACH VOLLEYBALL (ABOVE) The glamorous and fast-growing spin-off of the traditional court sport will make its Olympic début in Atlanta

SPRINTS

If the men's 1500m is the Blue Riband event of the Olympic Games, then the most exciting race is the 100m sprint. To the winner goes the glory and immediate recognition as the world's fastest man. The race lasts 10 seconds, but there is enormous excitement. The start is breathtaking, runners almost exploding out of their blocks; 20 strides to half-way; another 15 and it is almost over, just a last desperate dive to the tape.

MICHAEL JOHNSON (USA) IS A PHENOMENON, A SPRINTER WITH AN EFFORTLESS, UPRIGHT STYLE THAT DEFIES THE COACHING MANUALS. UNBEATABLE OVER 200M BEFORE THE 1992 OLYMPICS, HE PICKED UP A VIRUS AND FAILED TO REACH THE FINAL. HE WON THE 400M TITLE AT THE 1993 WORLD CHAMPIONSHIPS, AND BOTH 200M AND 400M IN 1995. HE IS A HOT FAVOURITE TO WIN GOLD IN ATLANTA – TWO IF THE SCHEDULE IS NOT TOO UNKIND.

There are three distances in the sprints: 100m, 200m and 400m, being a quarter (one straight), a half (one bend and straight) and a complete lap respectively. Men and women compete in all three events and each race is run strictly in lanes. One foot on the line and a runner may be disqualified – the fate that befell Gwen Torrance (USA) in the 1995 World Championship 200m.

The distances are measured from the inside of the track, so in the longer sprints the start is staggered – runners in the outside lanes starting further up the track. The stagger works out only as the runners go down the finishing straight.

The start is vital in sprinting, and competitors use starting blocks to give themselves extra leverage. They are adjustable and runners nail them to the track so that their hands almost touch the starting line in each lane. Runners guilty of a false start have a warning light switched on behind their blocks and a second infringement in that race will result in disqualification.

American domination

The United States have largely dominated Olympic sprinting, especially the men's competition, and they have virtually monopolized the world records. In the five Games between

DIP FOR THE TAPE **Donovan Bailey (CAN, 271) wins the 1995 World Championship 100m title**

MARIE-JOSE PEREC (FRA), FRENCH RECORD-HOLDER IN THE 100M, 200M, 400M AND 400M HURDLES, CONFIRMED HER SUPREMACY IN THE WOMEN'S 400M WHEN SHE FOLLOWED UP HER 1991 WORLD TITLE BY WINNING OLYMPIC GOLD IN BARCELONA. PEREC, BORN IN GUADELOUPE, CONTESTED THE 200M IN THE 1993 WORLD CHAMPIONSHIPS AND WAS JUST OUT OF THE MEDALS BEHIND MERLENE OTTEY. BACK TO 400M IN 1995, SHE WON THE WORLD TITLE AGAIN, AND BUT FOR HAMSTRING TROUBLE WOULD HAVE ATTEMPTED THE 400M HURDLES, TOO.

1932 and 1956, for example, American male 200m runners took 13 of the 15 medals available to them, losing only two bronzes.

American men have won both the 200m and 400m 15 times and the 100m on 14 occasions. Such is the strength in depth of US sprinting – and so strict are their Olympic trials qualification rules – that their top sprinters are sometimes omitted, as Carl Lewis – the first man to successfully defend his Olympic 100m title – found out in 1992.

FOUR GOLDS IN ONE GAMES

TWO AMERICAN SPRINTERS HAVE WON FOUR TITLES IN ONE GAMES, THE 100M/200M DOUBLE, THE SPRINT RELAY AND THE LONG JUMP – JESSE OWENS IN 1936 AND CARL LEWIS IN 1984. THE ONLY WOMAN TO EQUAL THIS FEAT IS FANNY BLANKERS-KOEN (NED), WHO IN 1948 BROUGHT OFF THE 100/200M DOUBLE, THE 80M HURDLES AND THE RELAY.

Women's sprinting

Women first took part in Olympic track and field in 1928, when there was a 100m event. The 200m was added in 1948, and the 400m in 1964. Americans have an outstanding record in the 100m and 200m. Wyomia Tyus was the first woman sprinter to successfully defend an Olympic sprint title, the 100m in 1968.

There have been several dual 100m/200m winners, but Valerie Brisco-Hooks (USA) is the only woman to bring off the 200m/400m double, in 1984. Perhaps the greatest achievement of all was that of Betty Cuthbert (AUS), who at 18 won the 100m and 200m at the 1956 Games by wide margins and anchored the Australian relay team to victory, and, after injury kept her out in 1960, returned to the Olympic scene in 1964 and won the 400m gold medal.

First out of the blocks

Linford Christie (GBR) won the 100m title in 1992 at the age of 32. Any doubts that he was the world's No.1 were dispelled in the 1993 World Championships when he won in 9.87sec, 0.01sec outside the world record. Injury kept Christie out of the medals in 1995 – Donovan Bailey (CAN) won gold – but he remains a force.

Challenging the Americans over 200m will be the 1993 world champion Frankie Fredericks (NAM), the African country he has put on the Olympic map. But Michael Johnson (USA) ended the 1995 season with 27 straight wins over 200m or 400m – 48 wins in a row over 400m!

Gail Devers and Gwen Torrence will probably spearhead the American challenge in the women's 100m/200m sprints. Irina Privalova (RUS) and Merlene Ottey (JAM) will certainly be in the running. And Marie-Jose Perec (FRA) will be dangerous in whichever event she chooses to contest, as will Cathy Freeman (AUS), who achieved the 200m/400m double at the 1994 Commonwealth Games.

MIDDLE-DISTANCE

The most glamorous event in athletics is the men's 1500m, the Blue Riband of the track. Some of the greatest names in the athletics history have won the 1500m Olympics gold medal, from Paavo Nurmi (FIN) in the twenties, Herb Elliott (AUS) and Peter Snell (NZE) in the sixties, to Sebastian Coe (GBR) in the eighties. Coe is the only man to win successive gold medals.

Two races come into the category of middle-distance: the 800m and 1500m, both run by men and women. The 800m – over two laps – has a staggered start and is run in lanes until the end of the first bend, after which the runners may break for the inside. The 1500m – over 3¾ laps – is started on a curved line, with runners moving inside as soon as they are able to.

Tactics

Part of the attraction of middle-distance races for the spectator is the tactical manoeuvring involved. Runners with a fast finish play a waiting game, pouncing as late as possible to take the lead, while those with less speed try to draw the sting out of their rivals by keeping up a fast pace.

The 800m often sees bumping and boring as runners try to avoid being boxed in when the race hots up. But a runner may be disqualified for deliberate physical contact. There is a dilemma, though, because running too wide adds metres to the distance – more than six metres per lap for every metre away from the inside.

Tips for the top

One of the biggest "certainties" going into the 1996 Olympics is Noureddine Morceli (ALG) in the men's 1500m. Three-times World Champion, and multi-world-record holder over a range of distances, he suffered the only serious setback of his remarkable career in the 1992 Games, when, trapped on the kerb in a slow-run race, he was well beaten by Fermin Cacho (ESP). The Spaniard has since been a long way behind in two world championships, and it is difficult to see who can prevent Morceli crowning his career with an Olympic gold. Among his rivals will be the young Italian-based Venuste Niyongabo (BDI), but Morceli's ability to force the pace himself means he is unlikely to make the same mistake again.

MARIA MUTOLA (MOZ) FIRST CAME TO NOTICE WHEN, DESPITE RUNNING LIKE A NOVICE, SHE CAME FOURTH IN THE 1991 WORLD CHAMPIONSHIPS 800M. TRAINING IN THE USA ON A SCHOLARSHIP, SHE CAME FIFTH IN THE 1992 OLYMPICS AND THEN WON THE WORLD TITLE IN 1993. HER DISQUALIFICATION IN 1995 WAS FOR RUNNING OUT OF HER LANE, BUT IF MUTOLA CAN GET HER ACT TOGETHER AT ATLANTA SHE WILL BE HARD TO BEAT.

GREAT DANE Wilson Kipketer (369) was born in Kenya, but he now runs for Denmark

THE BLUE RIBAND

THE COUNTRY WHICH HAS WON MOST GOLD MEDALS IN THE 1500M IS GREAT BRITAIN, WITH FIVE – CHARLES BENNETT (1900), ARNOLD JACKSON (1912), ALBERT HILL (1920) AND SEBASTIAN COE (1980 AND 1984). THE 1952 WINNER WAS JOSEF BARTHEL (LUX) – THE ONLY CHAMPION EVER PRODUCED BY THE TINY GRAND DUCHY IN THE SUMMER GAMES.

NOUREDDINE MORCELI (ALG) IS THE OUTSTANDING ATHLETE OF THIS, AND PERHAPS ANY, AGE. WORLD CHAMPION AT 1500M IN 1991, 1993 AND 1995, HE HAS SET WORLD RECORDS AT 1500M (3MIN 27.37SEC), ONE MILE (3MIN 44.29SEC), 2,000M (4MIN 47.88SEC) AND 3,000M (7MIN 25.11SEC). HE AIMS TO HOLD EVERY MARK FROM 800M TO 10,000M. HIS SHOCK DEFEAT IN THE 1992 GAMES WILL SPUR HIM ON TO SUCCESS IN ATLANTA.

Such is the supremacy of African middle- and long-distance running that they could make a clean sweep of the men's events in 1996. The most likely man to prevent this is, paradoxically, a Kenyan, Wilson Kipketer, now a naturalized Dane, who won the world 800m in 1995 more or less as he liked.

Hassiba Boulmerka (ALG) flew the flag for African women when she won the 1992 1500m, but she was given a tough race in the 1995 World Championships by Kelly Holmes (GBR), who had to be content with a minor medal in the 800m, too. Holmes returned to the sport only three years ago and could challenge strongly at both distances.

In the 800m, Holmes may not have to face her Gothenburg conqueror, the brave Ana Quirot (CUB), who came back to win the world title at 32 after nearly losing her life in a domestic fire two years earlier. But the one to beat may well be Maria Mutola (MOZ), the 1993 champion who was disqualified in the semi-finals.

LONG-DISTANCE

Watching athletes pounding round the track for lap after lap has a peculiar fascination for spectators, who can only sit and wonder at how modern long-distance runners keep up a stamina-sapping pace for so long and then find the extra to produce those last-lap sprints.

Men have been running the 5,000m and 10,000m in the Olympics since 1912 – the 5k and 10k, as they are also known. But such distances are relatively new to women. A 3,000m race was introduced in 1984, and this will convert to 5,000m in Atlanta. The 10,000m was first included at the 1988 Games.

Ever decreasing times

The rate at which these races are now run almost puts them in the middle-distance category, with the world-record pace for the men's 5k having dipped to below 64 seconds per lap.

The first requisite of a distance runner is stamina. Style does not seem to matter, as evidenced by the variety of styles exhibited by runners of varying build and length of stride. What they all have in common, however, is a dedicated training programme in which they clock up thousands of miles a year.

Judgement of pace is vitally important during a race. Fields are larger than for the middle-distance events, 16 in the 5k and 20 in the 10k. If a strong pace is set from the beginning, the field soon gets strung out behind the leaders. Often a group of six or seven breaks away, and this might be whittled down to two or three before the final surge for the tape.

Men to watch

In the 1995 world championships, Africans filled the first six places in the men's 5,000m and 10,000m, an extraordinary statistic. Apart from the intervention of the remarkable Lasse Viren (FIN) in the seventies, few athletes have challenged the might of Africa since the "high-altitude" Olympics at Mexico City in 1968, when African runners made a clean sweep of the medals in the 5k and 10k. It has become clear that training at altitude is extremely beneficial in the distance events.

Distance runners don't just come from Kenya and Ethiopia, but they have been coming from North Africa, too, first Tunisia and then Morocco. It is difficult to see anyone from another continent preventing a clean sweep of the medals in Atlanta.

Double world record-holder Haile Gebresilasie (ETH) can expect the biggest challenges to come from the Moroccans and Kenyans – but which individual is difficult to predict. Both countries seem to be churning out world-class distance runners at will. Khalid Skah (MOR) controversially won the Barcelona 10k, but in the 1995 World Championships, having had his training curtailed because of a stress fracture, he finished second behind Gebresilasie, with another Moroccan fourth and Kenyans third, fifth and sixth. In the shorter event, another three Moroccans finished in the first six, but they could not beat defending champion Ismael Kirui (KEN).

SONIA O'SULLIVAN (IRE) STAKED HER CLAIM TO OLYMPIC CONTENTION WITH AN OUTSTANDING 5K TRIUMPH IN THE 1995 WORLD CHAMPIONSHIPS. COMMENTING ON THE ABSENCE OF THE CHINESE AT GOTHENBURG BECAUSE THEY WERE IN TRAINING FOR ATLANTA, THE EUROPEAN 3K CHAMPION SAID: "SO AM I," MAINTAINING THAT THE CHINESE HELD NO FEARS FOR HER. SHE WENT ON TO WIN A SHARE OF THE "GOLDEN FOUR" BONUS (IN GOLD BARS) FOR HER FOUR 5K VICTORIES IN THE GRANDS PRIX.

Fleet of foot

Contenders for the women's distance events come from a far wider base. The Chinese are an unknown quantity, but cannot be ignored. They showed promise in the 1992 Olympics, but were nothing short of sensational in the 1993 World Championships, with gold in the 1500m, all three medals in the 3,000m and gold and silver in the 10,000m, and later that year set world records in all three events. Their absence from the 1995 World Championships was a surprise.

We do know the form, however, of the other contenders. Derartu Tulu (ETH) underlined the rise of African women's distance running with her 10k triumph in the 1992 Olympics. Despite a winter injury which seriously interrupted her training, it took a last-lap surge by Fernanda Ribeiro (POR) – world 5k record-holder – to beat her for the 1995 10k world title. Then Ribeiro, understandably tired, had to give way to the extremely impressive Sonia O'Sullivan (IRE) in the 5,000m. Someone who should not be discounted for the 10,000m in 1996 is former world champion Liz McColgan (GBR), whose sixth place in 1995 was an encouraging performance after a long absence through injury.

HAILE GEBRESILASIE (ETH) SET A WORLD 5K RECORD OF 12M 56.96SEC IN 1994 TO KNOCK 1.43SEC OFF THE SEVEN-YEAR-OLD MARK POSTED BY THE GREAT SAID AOUITA (MOR). HE BRIEFLY LOST THIS IN 1995 TO MOSES KIPTANUI (KEN), BUT REGAINED IT ON AUGUST 16 WITH ONE OF THE MOST ASTONISHING RUNS IN TRACK HISTORY. HIS TIME OF 12M 44.39SEC SLASHED JUST UNDER 11 SECONDS OFF THE OLD RECORD. EARLIER IN THE YEAR HE HAD CAPTURED THE 10K RECORD WITH 26M 43.53SEC BEFORE TAKING THE WORLD TITLE.

MARATHON

Some of the most dramatic stories in Olympic history have come in the marathon. The courage of little Dorando Pietri (ITA), repeatedly falling and staggering towards the tape in the 1908 Games remains one of sport's most enduring images.

DIFFERENT DISTANCES

THE 1908 RACE WAS RUN FROM WINDSOR CASTLE TO WHITE CITY STADIUM IN LONDON, AND THE DISTANCE, 42,195M (26MI 385YD), BECAME THE STANDARD MARATHON DISTANCE FROM THE 1924 GAMES. OTHER DISTANCES WERE: 40,000M (1896 AND 1904), 40,260M (1900), 41,860M (1906), 40,200 (1912) AND 42,750M (1920). IF RUN AROUND A 400M TRACK, THE MARATHON WOULD INVOLVE 5M SHORT OF 105½ LAPS.

The marathon race was devised for the first modern Games, in 1896, inspired by the legend of the ancient Greek messenger Pheidippedes, who ran 38.6km from Marathon to Athens to deliver news of a victory in battle before dropping dead.

The first Olympic marathon to be run on an out-and-back course – starting and finishing in the stadium – was at Stockholm in 1912. Women first competed in 1984.

Running the marathon

Marathon training is a way of life. An athlete will run 25-30km a day almost every day of the year. This includes distance work, running at the rate of around 1km every 3 minutes, speed work and rest.

Running for more than two hours takes the athlete into new frontiers, where, especially in hot weather, dehydration, exhaustion and blisters are all dangers. Marathon runners must replace the huge amount of liquid lost, and refreshment stations are situated at regular intervals where drinks and water for cooling the athlete are available.

Take your pick

Predicting the winner of the Olympic marathon is a hazardous pastime; there are so many imponderables. Times, also, are only an imprecise guide to performance, as courses around the world differ in severity. That is why there are no world records for the marathon, only "world bests".

In the 1992 Olympics, 112 athletes took part in the men's marathon, won by Young-Cho Hwang (KOR) in 2h 13m 23s. In the women's race, Valentina Yegorova (EUN) beat 46 rivals in 2h 32m 41s.

Using the 1995 World Championships as a guide, the men's winner Martin Fiz (ESP) will have a favourite's chance in Atlanta. Kenyans, however, filled three of the first five places in the 1995 Berlin marathon. The winner, Sammy Lelei, recorded the second-fastest time ever, 2h 7m 3s.The women's 1995 World Championship marathon was a fiasco, being run 400m short, but the winner, Manuela Machado (POR), will be a strong candidate in 1996.

MACHADO'S MARATHON **The Portuguese star (centre), runner-up in 1993, won the 1995 World Championship marathon, but it was run 400m short**

RELAYS

The secret of good relay running is slick baton changing. If a runner drops the baton during an exchange, or it happens outside the strictly controlled area, then the whole team is automatically disqualified.

USA AS USUAL Butch Reynolds hands over to Michael Johnson for the anchor leg of the 4 x 400m relay at the 1995 World Championships

There are two relays for men and women: 4 x 100m and 4 x 400m. All employ staggered starts, and runners must stay in their team's lane in the shorter event. But in the 4 x 400m, runners on the second leg may break to the inside on reaching the back straight. The final – "anchor" – runner must pass the finishing line holding the baton.

Both men's relays were first held in 1912; the women's 4 x 100m gained Olympic recognition in 1928, but the 4 x 400m was first run in 1972.

American monopoly

The USA has an incomparable record in the relays, which is perhaps not surprising for the country where relays were invented. Their 4 x 100m men's teams have never been outrun in Olympic competition: on the three occasions when they did not win the gold medal, they were disqualified. They have won the event 14 times, and on 12 of these they either equalled or broke the world record. In the 4 x 400m, the USA have won 13 of the 17 possible titles, setting nine world record marks and equalling it once.

The USA men's relay squads will again start as hot favourites, while the women's events may well be fought out between the USA and Russia.

WALKS

Though not the most glamorous Olympic competitors in many people's eyes, walkers are a dedicated bunch of athletes who put in miles of training.

There have been men's walks in the Olympics since 1908. The current distances – 50k (31mi, 123yd) and 20k (12mi, 753yd) – were first included in the Games in 1932 and 1956, respectively, and a women's 10k (6mi, 377yd) race was introduced in 1992.

Keeping flat-footed

Walking is defined by strict rules requiring constant contact with the ground and that the leg be momentarily straight as the foot touches the ground. The walker's characteristic wobbling gait results from their exaggerated swinging of the hips. Judges are posted along the route to scrutinize the walkers, who may be disqualified for "lifting" (the back foot, that is, before the front foot makes contact with the ground) or other misdemeanours. A card system warns the athletes and three cards means elimination.

WORLD WALKERS The field sets out from the stadium on the 50k World Championship walk

Men's walking honours have been shared by a contrasting variety of countries, from Mexico to Italy and Eastern Europe. Chinese women filled first, third and fifth places in the inaugural walk, albeit after the first-past-the-line Alina Ivanova (UKR) had been disqualified.

HURDLES

Few of the massive crowd at Los Angeles in 1984 who witnessed the final of the first women's Olympic 400 metres hurdles had heard of the winner, even though she was a student at Iowa State University. For this was not another in the long line of American champions, but Nawal El Moutawakel, the first Moroccan – she was sponsored by the King of Morocco – the first Arab woman, indeed the first African woman, to win an Olympic gold medal.

MASTER HURDLER

NO OTHER ATHLETE HAS DOMINATED AN EVENT TO THE EXTENT ED MOSES (USA) RULED 400M HURDLING FROM 1977 TO 1987, WHEN HE WON 122 CONSECUTIVE RACES. HE HAD ALREADY WON THE OLYMPIC TITLE IN 1976, WOULD ALMOST CERTAINLY HAVE RETAINED IT IN 1980 BUT FOR THE AMERICAN BOYCOTT, AND THEN WON IT AGAIN IN 1984. HE BROKE THE WORLD RECORD FOUR TIMES, TAKING IT FROM 47.82 TO – IN 1983 – 47.02SEC.

The début of the women's 400m hurdles completed the Olympic programme of hurdle events, the 110m for men – 100m for women – and 400m now for both. A 100m men's event was contested in 1896, and became the 110m from 1900, and at the same Games the one-lap race was introduced. In 1900 and 1904 there was also a 200m hurdles.

The first Olympic high hurdles for women took place at Los Angeles, in 1932, when it was held over 80 metres. The inaugural event was won by the great all-round American athlete Mildred "Babe" Didrikson. It became the 100m hurdles in 1972.

SPRINTER-HURDLER Gail Devers (USA, centre), who won the Olympic 100m flat at Barcelona in 1992, retained her World Championship 100m hurdles title at Gothenberg in 1995

Going for gold

Men's hurdling has been largely dominated by the USA. At one stage, between 1948 and 1960, they took all 12 high hurdles Olympic medals as well as eight at 400m, including the four golds. Colin Jackson (GBR) – who set a world record with 12.91sec in the 1993 110m hurdles World Championships – is a strong contender but he has a bad record in major events. Mark McCoy (CAN), the 1992 champion, Andrew Jarrett (GBR) and the USA runners will be other leading candidates. In the longer event, Kevin Young (USA) – who broke the world record winning gold in Barcelona – will again be favourite.

Sally Gunnell (GBR) is the reigning Olympic 400m hurdles champion, but injury in 1995 forced her to sit and watch Kim Batten (USA) take both her world title and her world record. They are the top two. Over the shorter distance, Yordanka Donkova (BUL) and Gail Devers (USA) are hot tips.

OBSTACLE HEIGHTS

EVENT	HEIGHT	DISTANCE APART
WOMEN'S 100M HURDLES	84 CM (2FT, 9IN)	8.5M (9YD, 1FT)
MEN'S 110M HURDLES	106.7 CM (3FT, 6IN)	9.14M (10YD)
WOMEN'S 400M HURDLES	76.2 CM (2FT, 6IN)	35M (38YD, 1FT, 6IN)
MEN'S 400M HURDLES	91.4 CM (3FT)	35M (38YD, 1FT, 6IN)
MEN'S 3,000M STEEPLECHASE	91.4 CM (3FT)	4 PER LAP
WATER JUMP	91.4CM (3FT) + 3.66M (12FT) SPLASH	1 PER LAP

STEEPLECHASE

The steeplechase began as a cross-country race in 1850. It did not transfer to the track until the 1900 Olympics, and it was standardized in its present form only in 1954.

MOSES KIPTANUI (KEN) WAS CRITICIZED FOR SLOWING DOWN WHEN WINNING HIS THIRD WORLD STEEPLECHASE TITLE AT GOTHENBURG WHEN IN SIGHT OF HIS OWN WORLD RECORD. HE DULY BROKE IT FIVE DAYS LATER AT THE WELTKLASSE MEETING IN ZURICH, WHERE A REWARD OF ABOUT £80,000 WAS AVAILABLE FOR DOING SO. HIS TIME OF 7MIN 59.18SEC WAS AN ATHLETICS LANDMARK, THE FIRST STEEPLECHASE IN UNDER EIGHT MINUTES. KIPTANUI ALSO BRIEFLY HELD THE 5K WORLD RECORD IN 1995 BEFORE HAILE GEBRESILASIE (ETH) TOOK IT BACK THAT SAME NIGHT IN ZURICH. IN A 5K IN ZURICH, TWO WEEKS LATER, THE ETHIOPIAN COMFORTABLY BEAT KIPTANUI.

Only men compete in an Olympic steeplechase, which is run on the track over 3,000 metres, or 7½ laps. There are five barriers per lap, four fixed hurdles and one water jump, although the hurdles are removed for the first half-lap. The race is not run in lanes. As the race is not run in lanes, all the runners take the same 3.96m (13ft) wide hurdles.

Runners normally clear the hurdles, but place their leading foot on the water-jump barrier (spikes on the far side), pushing off to land in the shallow part of the water and continue without breaking stride.

A Kenyan domain

The Kenyans hi-jacked the Olympic steeplechase in the eighties and have not released their stranglehold. Kenyan "interest" in the steeplechase first came to the fore in the 1968 Olympics, when schoolboy Amos Biwott, a relative novice in the event, amused the crowd with his clumsy jumping and erratic running before coming from nowhere to take the gold medal in front of his compatriot Benjamin Kogo. In 1972, the great middle-distance runner Kip Keino (KEN) briefly turned his attentions to the steeplechase and won gold, with compatriot Benjamin Jipcho second.

In 1992, Kenya, led by Matthew Birir, had a clean sweep of the medals and could probably have provided another three to beat the rest. Kenya have also won all three world steeplechase titles in the nineties, through one man, Moses Kiptanui, and he will be one of the hottest favourites for an Olympic gold medal in Atlanta.

MASTER-CHASER Moses Kiptanui (KEN) takes the water jump at the 1995 World Championships

JUMPS

JAVIER SOTOMAYOR (CUB) BECAME THE FIRST MAN TO HIGH JUMP 8FT (2.44M), WHEN HE BROKE THE WORLD RECORD IN 1989, A MARK HE EXTENDED TO 2.45M IN 1993. HE WON OLYMPIC GOLD IN 1992 AND THE WORLD TITLE IN 1993.

The most successful jumper of all time performed at the turn of the century. Ray Ewry (USA) won eight gold medals in 1900, 1904 and 1908. His speciality was the standing jump and he won every event he entered: the standing long and standing high jumps three times each, and the standing triple jump in 1900 and 1904.

The four current jumping events have always been on the men's Olympic programme, but when women's athletics first appeared in the Games, in 1928, only the high jump was included. The long jump followed in 1948, the triple jump makes its début in 1996, and the pole vault – only recently taken up seriously by women – is not yet on the programme.

Jumping rules

In the high jump and pole vault, the bar is raised after each round of jumps, a round being completed when all the competitors have either cleared the height, passed, or been eliminated after three consecutive failures. The winner is the one with the highest clearance. If two or more clear the same height before failing, a count-back system determines placings according to failures. Competitors, when it is their turn, may take their jump or pass, but, once they pass on a height, cannot make another attempt until the bar has been raised.

In the long and triple jumps finals, the best eight jumpers after three rounds have three more attempts. The longest jump wins, with ties broken by the second best efforts.

In all four events, qualifying takes place a day before the final. Jumpers have three attempts to reach a qualifying mark. If fewer than 12 jumpers accomplish this, the final group is made up to 12 with the best of the rest.

CUBAN THREAT New long-jumping sensation, 1995 world champion Ivan Pedrosa (CUB), threatens US supremacy in this event

High Jump

Dick Fosbury (USA) revolutionized the event when he won the Olympic title in 1968 with his head-first, on-the-back style, and the "Fosbury flop", as it was dubbed, is now used almost universally.

The reigning Olympic champion and world record holder, Javier Sotomayor (CUB), was injured when he lost his world title in 1995 on a count-back to Troy Kemp (BAH). Sotomayor should still be favourite to become the first man to win the Olympic title twice.

Two women, Iolanda Balas (ROM) – in 1960 and 1964 – and Ulrike Meyfarth (FRG) – in 1972 and, remarkably, in 1984 – have won the gold medal twice. Stefka Kostadinova (BUL) won the world title in 1987 – with a world record 2.09m – and then again, as a 30-year-old mother of seven months, in 1995.

Pole Vault

The USA won every Olympic gold medal until 1972, when reigning champion Bob Seagren had his favourite "Cata-pole" banned shortly before the Games. He was beaten into second place by

JONATHAN EDWARDS (GBR), AT 29 AND WITH AN UNEXCEPTIONAL CAREER APPARENTLY WINDING DOWN, SUDDENLY REACHED A NEW LEVEL IN 1995. AFTER FOUR WIND-ASSISTED 18M TRIPLE JUMPS (INCLUDING ONE OF 18.43M), HE BROKE THE 10-YEAR-OLD WORLD RECORD BY A CENTIMETRE WITH 17.98M. AT THE WORLD CHAMPIONSHIPS HE LEAPT 18.29M, THE FIRST LEGAL 60FT TRIPLE JUMP AND 67CM FARTHER THAN THE RUNNER-UP.

Wolfgang Nordwig (FRG), since when the USA have never won the title.

Sergey Bubka (URS/UKR) has virtually made the event his own, except for his unaccountable elimination in the 1992 Olympics, and the five-times world champion is expected to gain his second Olympic gold medal in Atlanta. His leading challengers may come from three strong Russians and a young South African vaulter, Okkert Brits.

Long Jump

The USA have won the gold medal 19 times in the 21 Games they have entered. Carl Lewis (USA) won his third straight Olympic title in 1992. Double world champion, and Olympic runner-up, Mike Powell (USA), will try again, but Ivan Pedroso (CUB) could be the favourite. He won the 1995 world title and passed Powell's world record with a jump of 8.96m, but it was not ratified.

Recent major women's honours have been shared by Jackie Joyner-Kersee (USA) and Heike Drechsler (GDR/GER). But both were well down the field in the 1995 world championships, won with only 6.98m by British-born Fiona May (ITA).

Triple Jump

Viktor Saneyev (USSR) won three consecutive titles from 1968, and was only narrowly beaten for a fourth in 1980. Jonathan Edwards (GBR) took the event into a new era in 1995, winning the world title with the first ever legal 18m jump. Brian Wellman (BER), Yoelvis Quesada (CUB) and the 1992 champion, Mike Conley (USA), will be strong threats to Edwards.

Inessa Kravets (UKR), the 1992 long-jump silver medallist, destroyed the field in the 1995 World Championships with a triple jump of 15.50m. It broke the world record by 41cm and established her as a hot tip for Atlanta.

SERGEY BUBKA (UKR), UNIQUELY, HAS WON GOLD AT EVERY WORLD CHAMPIONSHIP IN THE POLE VAULT, AND SET 35 WORLD RECORDS, OFTEN EXTENDING THE MARK BY AS LITTLE AS A CENTIMETRE OR TWO. HE WON THE OLYMPIC TITLE IN 1988, AND BECAME THE FIRST 6-METRE AND 20-FOOT JUMPER, BUT FAILED TO CLEAR HIS FIRST HEIGHT (5.70M) IN BARCELONA.

THROWS

Throwing events are a staple of Olympic Games athletics, having originated in the Ancient Games. The javelin – after all – is only a modern version of spear throwing.

The discus event was included in the first modern Games in 1896, along with the shot put. The hammer was added in 1900, the javelin in 1908. The advent of women's athletics in the Olympics saw the introduction of the discus in 1928, followed by the javelin in 1932 and the shot put in 1948. Women do not throw the hammer.

Throwing requirements

In addition to strength and technique, speed is an important factor in throwing events, whether it be on the long javelin run-up or across the short shot-put circle. The missiles have standard weights and dimensions, the women's being lighter than the men's. The actual methods of throwing are also strictly regulated.

The shot, discus and hammer are thrown from circular concrete slabs. Competitors must stay within the circle while throwing and until the missile lands, and then step out of the back of the circle. Throws, which must land in marked sectors, are measured from the front of the circle to the spot where the missile first hits the ground. In the javelin, competitors must not step over the white "scratch" line that marks the end of the runway. The javelin must land point first, although it does not have to stick in the ground.

As with the jumping events, Olympian throwers take part in a qualifying competition, with those reaching a set distance in a maximum of three attempts, or the top 12, going through to the final. In the finals, the leading eight after three attempts have another three. The medals are decided – quite simply – by the longest individual throws.

ZHIHONG HUANG (CHN) BECAME HER COUNTRY'S FIRST WORLD ATHLETICS CHAMPION WHEN SHE WON THE SHOT PUT AT TOKYO IN 1991. SHE WON A SILVER MEDAL IN THE 1992 OLYMPICS AND RETAINED HER WORLD TITLE IN 1993. HOWEVER, SHE LOST HER CROWN TO ASTRID KUMBERNUSS (GER) IN 1995.

Tradition

The USA have an excellent tradition in the men's shot and discus, winning nearly every Olympic competition until the seventies, when the pendulum of success swung right across to Eastern Europe. In the hammer, too, the USA enjoyed early domination, but after the Second World War the spoils were shared largely between the USSR and Hungary. Only once have the USA tasted javelin success – when Cy Young won in 1952. The country with the finest tradition of javelin throwing has been Finland, who have accumulated seven gold medals over the years.

The outstanding competitor in any throwing event has to be Al Oerter (USA), whose four gold medals – from 1956 to 1968 inclusive – remains unparalleled in any individual Olympic event.

The women's throwing events have been dominated by Europeans. Athletes from the former Soviet Union have always excelled in the

JAN ZELEZNY (CZE) KILLED OFF THE OPPOSITION IN BARCELONA WITH HIS FIRST THROW, AN OLYMPIC RECORD OF 89.66M (294FT 6IN), TO WIN THE JAVELIN GOLD MEDAL HE SO NARROWLY MISSED IN SEOUL IN 1988 – WHEN TAPIO KORJUS (FIN) BEAT HIM BY 16CM (6¼IN) WITH THE LAST THROW OF THE COMPETITION. ZELEZNY, WORLD CHAMPION IN 1993 AND 1995, CAME TO BOTH OLYMPICS AS THE WORLD-RECORD HOLDER, AND IT IS UNLIKELY THAT ANYONE WILL BREAK HIS 1993 MARK OF 95.65M (313FT 10IN) BEFORE ATLANTA.

shot, and they have shared discus success with their fellow Eastern Europeans. In 1992, however, the gold medal went to Maritza Marten (CUB), the first non-European winner for 60 years. The first javelin champion was the famous Mildred "Babe" Didrikson (USA), but the title has almost always gone to a European, East or West.

Looking forward

The traditionally strong throwing countries will produce most of the leading contenders again in Atlanta. The USA are likely to continue their "comeback" in the shot, begun by world-record holder Randy Barnes in 1990 and continued by 1992 Olympic winner Mike Stulce and the young 1995 world champion John Godina.

The superior technique and speed across the circle of discus world champion Lars Riedel (GER) should keep him ahead of his rivals. And the ability of javelin world champion and record holder Jan Zelezny (CZE) to pull out a really big throw when it matters most bodes well in defence of his title. The former Soviets, headed by reigning Olympic champion and double world champion Andrey Abduvaliyev (TJK), provided seven of the 12 hammer finalists in the 1995 world championships and will probably be out in similar force in Atlanta.

China has produced World Championship gold-medallists in all three women's throws in the nineties, notably Zhihong Huang, who twice won the shot, came second in 1995 and won an Olympic silver in 1992. The former Soviets are strong in the discus, as are Cuba, particularly reigning champion Maritza Marten. Javelin honours have been shared around in the nineties, with Natalya Shikolenko (BLR) beating her rivals in the 1995 World Championships to secure her first gold medal.

MULTI-EVENTS

The most gruelling events at the Olympics are the multi-events – the men's decathlon and the women's heptathlon. The track and field events – ten for men, seven for women – are held over two days and require many different attributes, as well as stamina.

Athletes compete for points in each event, awarded for their performance – time or distance – according to standard tables. The disciplines are contested as regular events except for two differences: competitors are allowed three false starts on the track, but have only three attempts on the field. Athletes who fail to take part in any event are eliminated from the contest.

Decathlon

A 10-event "All-Around Championship" was held in 1904, but the first true decathlon took place at Stockholm in 1912. Jim Thorpe (USA) took the gold medal by a considerable margin – as he did in the short-lived pentathlon. Other great decathletes include Bob Mathias (USA), who was only 17 when he won in 1948 and in the next Games became the first man to win it twice, and Daley Thompson (GBR), who emulated him in 1980 and 1984 and, with his enthusiasm and showmanship, did much to popularize the event.

Heptathlon

The first multi-event contest for women in the Olympics was the pentathlon, introduced in 1964, when it comprised the 80m hurdles, shot, high jump, long jump and 200m. In 1980, the 200m was replaced by the 800m, and in 1984 the event was replaced by the current heptathlon, with the 200m and javelin added to the existing five.

European countries produced all the five pentathlon winners, but the heptathlon has become almost synonymous with the name of Jackie Joyner-Kersee (USA), who came second in 1984 – Glynis Nunn (AUS) took gold – and won it in 1988 and 1992. But she will have to be in top form if she is to overcome the 1995 world champion, Ghada Shouaa (SYR), in Atlanta.

DAN O'BRIEN (USA), THE 1991 WORLD CHAMPION, MISSED THE 1992 GAMES THANKS TO "NO-HEIGHTING" THE POLE VAULT, IN THE UNFORGIVING US TRIALS. A MONTH AFTER WATCHING HIS COMPATRIOTS COLLECT ONLY A BRONZE AT BARCELONA, HE BEAT DALEY THOMPSON'S 8-YEAR-OLD WORLD RECORD WITH 8,891 POINTS.

SCHEDULE OF EVENTS

	DECATHLON	HEPTATHLON
1st day	100M LONG JUMP SHOT PUT HIGH JUMP 400M	100M HURDLES HIGH JUMP SHOT PUT 200M
2nd day	110M HURDLES DISCUS POLE VAULT JAVELIN 1500M	LONG JUMP JAVELIN 800M

MEDALS TABLE MEN

100m		
1		
2		
3		

200m		
1		
2		
3		

400m		
1		
2		
3		

800m		
1		
2		
3		

1500m		
1		
2		
3		

5,000m		
1		
2		
3		

10,000m		
1		
2		
3		

MARATHON		
1		
2		
3		

110m HURDLES		
1		
2		
3		

400m HURDLES		
1		
2		
3		

3,000m STEEPLECHASE		
1		
2		
3		

4 x 100m RELAY		
1		
2		
3		

4 x 400m RELAY
1
2
3

20Km WALK
1
2
3

50Km WALK
1
2
3

HIGH JUMP
1
2
3

LONG JUMP
1
2
3

TRIPLE JUMP
1
2
3

POLE VAULT
1
2
3

SHOT PUT
1
2
3

DISCUS
1
2
3

HAMMER
1
2
3

JAVELIN
1
2
3

DECATHLON
1
2
3

MEDALS TABLE WOMEN

100m
1
2
3

200m
1
2
3

400m
1
2
3

800m
1
2
3

1500m
1
2
3

5,000m
1
2
3

10,000m
1
2
3

MARATHON
1
2
3

100m HURDLES
1
2
3

400m HURDLES
1
2
3

4 x 100m RELAY
1
2
3

4 x 400m RELAY
1
2
3

10Km WALK
1
2
3

HIGH JUMP
1
2
3

LONG JUMP
1
2
3

TRIPLE JUMP
1
2
3

SHOT PUT
1
2
3

DISCUS
1
2
3

JAVELIN
1
2
3

HEPTATHLON
1
2
3

HOT HEPTATHLETE Jackie Joyner-Kersee (USA) also won long jump gold in 1988

SWIMMING

Men's swimming events in the 1896 Games were held in the cold, choppy waters of the Bay of Zea. In addition to three freestyle races, there was a 100m event confined to sailors anchored on ships in the port of Piraeus.

TRIPLE GOLD BACKSTROKER **Krisztina Egerszegi (HUN) has rediscovered her Olympic form**

MEDALS TABLE MEN

50m FREESTYLE		
1		
2		
3		

100m FREESTYLE		
1		
2		
3		

200m FREESTYLE		
1		
2		
3		

400m FREESTYLE		
1		
2		
3		

1500m FREESTYLE		
1		
2		
3		

100m BACKSTROKE		
1		
2		
3		

200m BACKSTROKE		
1		
2		
3		

100m BREASTSTROKE		
1		
2		
3		

It was 1908 before swimming events were held in a pool, 1912 before women swam in the Olympics, and 1948 before swimming went indoors. By 1968, women were competing in the same number of individual events as the men, 12, but in only two relays to the men's three, an imbalance that will be rectified in Atlanta with the inclusion of the women's 4 x 200m.

Swimming strokes

Swimming events encompass four different strokes and the medley, in which they are all used on separate legs. The front crawl is the fastest stroke; it is invariably swum in freestyle races – 50m, 100m, 200m, 400m and 1500m (800m for women). In the other three strokes – backstroke, breaststroke and butterfly – races are over 100m and 200m.

The medleys are 200m and 400m, with each stroke – in order butterfly, backstroke, breaststroke and freestyle – swum for 50m and 100m, respectively. The relays are 4 x 100m, 4 x 200m and 4 x 100m medley, in which the order is backstroke, breaststroke, butterfly and freestyle.

Competition

The Olympic pool is 50m long and has eight lanes about 2.5m wide. Races are started from blocks, except for backstroke events, which start in the water. Timing, to 0.001sec, is by individual electronic touch-pads at the finish. Swimmers must touch the end of the pool at each turn and keep in their lanes, which are marked with buoyed ropes on the surface. The three strokes are each governed by rules specifying not only the stroke itself but also the turn, and swimmers may be disqualified for not conforming to these.

Since the 1952 Games, the promotion of competitors from heats through to the final has been decided on time alone, not placings. There is no draw for lanes as position is based on the competitors' pre-Games best times for the first heats, and then on heat times. The swimmer with the fastest time is placed in lane 4, the next in lane 5, and so on through lanes 3, 6, 2, 7, 1, 8. This is called the "spearhead" principle, for the shape – if they race to form – the swimmers make in the water. The idea is to give the fastest swimmers a better chance to see and race against each other.

Making a big splash

American swimmers have always had an exceptional record in the Olympics, while

200m BREASTSTROKE

1		
2		
3		

100m BUTTERFLY

1		
2		
3		

200m BUTTERFLY

1		
2		
3		

200m INDIVIDUAL MEDLEY

1		
2		
3		

400m INDIVIDUAL MEDLEY

1		
2		
3		

4 x 100m FREESTYLE RELAY

1		
2		
3		

4 x 200m FREESTYLE RELAY

1		
2		
3		

4 x 100m MEDLEY RELAY

1		
2		
3		

MEDALS TABLE WOMEN

50m FREESTYLE

1		
2		
3		

100m FREESTYLE

1		
2		
3		

200m FREESTYLE

1		
2		
3		

400m FREESTYLE

1		
2		
3		

800m FREESTYLE

1		
2		
3		

100m BACKSTROKE

1		
2		
3		

200m BACKSTROKE

1		
2		
3		

100m BREASTSTROKE

1		
2		
3		

200m BREASTSTROKE

1		
2		
3		

100m BUTTERFLY

1		
2		
3		

200m BUTTERFLY

1		
2		
3		

200m INDIVIDUAL MEDLEY

1		
2		
3		

400m INDIVIDUAL MEDLEY

1		
2		
3		

4 x 100m FREESTYLE RELAY

1		
2		
3		

4 x 200m FREESTYLE RELAY

1		
2		
3		

4 x 100m MEDLEY RELAY

1		
2		
3		

Australia have produced many outstanding swimmers, especially in freestyle, and East Germany dominated women's swimming in the three Games they took part in from 1976.

In the 1990s, a new force in women's swimming emerged – China. They won four gold medals in the 1991 world championships, and another four in the Barcelona Olympics. Then, in the 1994 World Championships, they almost swept the board, winning nine of the 13 individual titles and all three relays. In three of the four races in which they were beaten, they came second, and they won three other silver medals and a bronze. They failed to win a medal only in the 800m.

Janet Evans (USA) is supreme in the 800m, Samantha Riley (AUS) beat off the Chinese challenge for both breaststroke events and the young prodigy Franziska Van Almsick (GER) is capable of winning any of the freestyle sprints.

And backstroker Krisztina Egerszegi (HUN) appeared to have recovered her Olympic form in the 1995 European Championships.

The US men have strength in depth and are still winning relays, but their disappointing 1992 Olympics, in which they won the two breaststroke and two butterfly golds, was followed by, for them, a disastrous 1994 world championships, with only one individual title. The Russians are particularly strong now, with Alexandr Popov outstanding in the 50m and 100m freestyle, and Kieran Perkins (AUS) will take some beating in the longer freestyle events, as will double 1994 world champion Norbert Rozsa (HUN) in the breaststroke.

KIERAN PERKINS (AUS) WON THE OLYMPIC 1500M TITLE IN 1992 AND WAS JUST TOUCHED OFF FOR FIRST PLACE IN THE 400M. IN 1994, HE WON BOTH EVENTS IN THE WORLD CHAMPIONSHIPS, AND SET WORLD RECORDS FOR THOSE AND THE 800M.

DIVING

As a leisure activity, diving goes naturally with swimming. But, as a sport, it is more akin to gymnastics and trampolining.

DIVING FOR GOLD Fu Mingxia (CHN), silhouetted against the brilliant Barcelona skyline, on her way to the highboard title in 1992

Highboard, or platform, diving made its Olympic début in 1904, springboard in 1908, with the women's events following in 1912 and 1920, respectively. Dives in highboard are made from a fixed board 10m above the water's surface, springboard from a springy board 3m from the water.

Take your pick

There are more than 80 standard dives to choose from. They are grouped as forward, backward, reverse, inward, twist and – for highboard – armstand dives, each incorporating manoeuvres such as somersaults, tucks and pikes. Every dive has a set "degree of difficulty", ranging from 1.2 for the simplest to 3.5 for the most difficult.

In competition, each dive is marked out of 10 by a panel of seven judges, with the highest and lowest marks discarded. The five remaining are totalled, then multiplied by the degree of difficulty to give the score for that competitor's dive.

In each event, entrants dive in a preliminary competition, the top 12 progressing to the final. Divers in the final perform two series of dives, one with restricted degree of difficulty, the other unrestricted; 10 in all. In each series, dives from different groups (forward, backward, etc.) must be chosen 24 hours before the competition starts and cannot then be changed.

Chinese takeover

Once a US-dominated sport, diving has virtually been "hijacked" by the Chinese, whose women have won every world title since 1986 and five of the six Olympic titles since 1984. The men have not quite had it all their own way, but in Atlanta the gold medals are most likely to go to their seemingly endless production line of brilliant divers. The US men will provide stiff competition, and Dmitri Saoutine (RUS) has recent narrow wins over his Chinese rivals in world competitions.

MEDALS TABLE MEN

SPRINGBOARD		
1		
2		
3		
PLATFORM		
1		
2		
3		
WATER POLO		
1		
2		
3		

MEDALS TABLE WOMEN

SPRINGBOARD		
1		
2		
3		
PLATFORM		
1		
2		
3		
SYNCHRO		
1		
2		
3		

WATER POLO

Water polo is a tough, skilful sport with plenty of action and shots at goal. Its followers will tell you that it is the world's most demanding team game.

Water polo requires strong swimming ability and there have been examples of crossover competitors. Paul Radomilovic (GBR) won water polo golds (1908, 1912 and 1920) and a relay gold (1908), and Johnny Weissmuller (USA) won five swimming golds (1924 and 1928) and a water polo bronze.

A seven-a-side team game, water polo has been a men's Olympic sport since 1900, although clubs, not countries, competed until 1908. Women also play water polo, but not as an Olympic sport.

Quick rules

The game is played over four periods of seven minutes in a 30 x 20m (98ft 5in x 65ft 7in) pool with a goal at each end. The goals are 3m (9ft 10in) wide and rise 90cm (2ft 11in) above the water.

Players may play the ball with one hand, in or out of the water, but only the goalkeeper can use both hands on the ball. The team in possession has 35 seconds in which to take a shot at goal. Each side has six reserves, but substitutions may be made only during intervals or at certain situations.

Teams to watch

Hungary have the best overall record in Olympic water polo, with six titles between 1932 and 1976. Yugoslavia won the tournament in 1984 and 1988 and looked set to dominate the sport. But because of UN sanctions they were banned from taking part in team games at Barcelona, where Italy beat Spain 9-8 in a bad-tempered final that went to three double periods of overtime, with the Unified Team taking bronze. In the 1994 World Championships Italy again overcame Spain in the final, with Russia finishing in third place, but a new name entered the equation in fourth, Croatia, who could take over in the Olympics where Yugoslavia left off.

SYNCHRO

Synchronized swimming, a recent addition to Olympic aquatic sports, is aptly described as "water ballet".

SMILING FOR THE JUDGES **The Mexican synchro duo in the preliminaries at the Barcelona Games**

A once derided sport, "synchro", as it is called, was introduced in 1984, with solo and duet events for women. In three Olympics all the gold and silver medals went to the USA and Canada. Remarkably, all six bronze medals went to Japan.

With out-of-sight plugs replacing the outrageous-looking nose clips, synchro is trying to live down its early Olympic image. The glitzy costumes and hairstyles are no more outlandish than those seen in ice skating. A technical programme is followed by a five-minute free routine, the swimmers performing under or on the water, matching artistic movements with music. Marks are awarded for both artistic impression and technical merit.

Change of emphasis

The solo and duet events have been replaced by an eight-woman team competition for Atlanta, but there is no reason to believe that the USA, Canada and Japan will not take the medals again.

GYMNASTICS

Gymnastics enjoyed a surge of popularity in the 1970s, when millions of television viewers thrilled first to the charismatic performances of the young Olga Korbut (URS) and then to the "perfection" of the even younger Nadia Comaneci (ROM).

The ancient Greeks built gymnasia for physical exercise, but gymnastics did not develop as a sport until the nineteenth century. A German teacher, Friedrich Ludwig Jahn, opened the first "turnplatz", an open-air gymnasium, in 1811. Known as the "father of modern gymnastics", Jahn developed exercises for apparatus in use and devised other gymnastics exercises.

Only men took part in the 1896 Games, and the gymnastics included all the apparatus in use today, and an event called "arm exercises with smooth cord" – rope climbing. The first time women competed in Olympic gymnastics was in 1928, but only in team events. It was not until 1952 that individual events for women were added.

Another branch of the sport, rhythmic gymnastics, practised by women, was accepted into the Olympics programme in 1984.

Marks out of ten

Competitors perform routines on the apparatus and are marked out of 10 by a panel of judges. Marks depend on the difficulty of the routines undertaken, how well they are performed and how smoothly the various elements of a routine are linked. Points are deducted for errors.

In the floor exercises, competitors perform spectacular front and back somersaults and handsprings, combined with balances on foot or

GYMNASTIC EVENTS

MEN	WOMEN
All-around	All-around
Floor exercise	Floor exercise
Horizontal bar	Balance beam
Parallel bars	Asymmetric bars
Pommel horse	Vault
Rings	Team
Vault	Rhythmic all-around
Team	Rhythmic group

VITALY SCHERBO (BLR), A 20-YEAR-OLD REPRESENTING THE UNIFIED TEAM (EX-USSR), DOMINATED THE MEN'S GYMNASTICS AT BARCELONA IN 1992, WINNING SIX GOLD MEDALS. YET HE WILL NEED TO BE AT HIS VERY BEST TO RETAIN HIS ALL-AROUND TITLE IN 1996, MISTAKES HAVING COST HIM HIS WORLD TITLE IN 1994, WHEN COMPATRIOT IVAN IVANKOV WON, AND HE WAS SECOND TO THE YOUNG LI XIAOSHUANG (CHN) IN 1995.

MEDALS TABLE MEN

ALL-AROUND		
1		
2		
3		

FLOOR		
1		
2		
3		

PARALLEL BARS		
1		
2		
3		

HORIZONTAL BAR		
1		
2		
3		

POMMEL HORSE		
1		
2		
3		

RINGS		
1		
2		
3		

VAULT		
1		
2		
3		

TEAM		
1		
2		
3		

MEDALS TABLE WOMEN

ALL-AROUND		
1		
2		
3		

FLOOR		
1		
2		
3		

BEAM		
1		
2		
3		

ASYMMETRIC BARS		
1		
2		
3		

VAULT		
1		
2		
3		

TEAM		
1		
2		
3		

RHYTHMIC ALL-AROUND		
1		
2		
3		

RHYTHMIC GROUP		
1		
2		
3		

hands, all smoothly linked. Men's routines feature strength movements and positions, while the women use dance steps and routines that match their movements to the music. Men's routines last 50–70sec, women's 60–90sec.

Gymnastic apparatus

The vault is the shortest event. Men have one jump, women two, only the better mark counting. A springboard is used to gain extra height at take-off. There is the flight onto the horse, a thrust to gain height, the flight off the horse and the landing, all important stages in the judging.

The asymmetric – uneven – bars, parallel bars and horizontal bar all feature swinging movements and changes of grip. The pommel horse and rings call for considerable arm and shoulder strength, because in these events gymnasts use only their hands to support themselves. The rings must be performed without swinging the ropes. For women, the beam is particularly difficult to master, as all the moves are performed on a surface only 10cm wide. Men perform under the bar, women on top of the beam.

The all-around and team events are separate competitions in which gymnasts perform on all the pieces of apparatus. The all-around – overall – champion is decided on the total points gained in the six (for men) or four (for women) events, the team medals by the aggregate of the four team members over their individual disciplines.

Rhythmic gymnastics

Competitors perform to music, using dance steps and graceful moves while they "juggle" with their "hand" apparatus. The individual events are the ribbon, hoop, rope, ball and clubs, but in Olympic competition one of these is dropped (the hoop in 1996) and there is only an all-around gold medal for individual competitors. A group event has been added for Atlanta, with competitors taking part in two exercises, the first with three ribbons and two balls, the second with all five using hoops.

ATLANTA HOPE
17-year-old Lilia Podkopayeva (UKR) won the 1995 World Championship all-around and vault gold medals

Gymnastics strongholds

Eastern European countries have dominated the Olympic gymnastics since the early 1950s, and Soviet gymnasts set Olympic records for medals won. Outside Eastern Europe, Japanese men have a good record, and more recently the United States and China have won gold medals.

The stronghold of rhythmic gymnastics is Eastern Europe, especially the former Soviet Union and Bulgaria.

BOXING

The world of professional boxing has sometimes fallen into disrepute, but none of the taints have ever besmirched the art of amateur boxing. Boxing at the Games has been above reproof. Indeed, the only controversy in amateur boxing has come in the scoring of fights.

Boxing is one of the world's oldest sports. It has appeared regularly in the Games since 1920, but had been included in 1904 and 1908. Two boxers have won gold medals in three Games, Laszlo Papp (HUN) – as a middleweight in 1948, then at light middleweight in 1952 and 1956 – and powerful heavyweight Teofilo Stevenson (CUB) in 1972, 1976 and 1980.

Generations of boxers have considered the Games a valuable stepping stone on the road to lucrative professional careers, and seven men have gone from gold medals to professional world heavyweight champion: Floyd Patterson (USA, middleweight, 1952), Cassius Clay (USA, light heavyweight, 1960), Joe Frazier (USA, heavyweight, 1964), George Foreman (USA, heavyweight, 1968), Michael and Leon Spinks (USA, middleweight and light heavyweight, respectively, 1976) and Lennox Lewis (CAN, super heavyweight, 1988). The Spinkses are the only brothers to win boxing gold medals in the same Games.

Competition

There are 12 weight classes in the boxing event, ranging from light flyweight (maximum weight 48kg – 105lb or 7st 7lb) to super heavyweight (minimum weight 91kg – 200lb or 14st 4lb). Each class is limited to 32 fighters, but some have many fewer. No boxer can appear at two weights and no country is permitted more than one boxer per class. The winner of each bout goes through; the loser is eliminated. Bronze medals are awarded to the losers of both semi-finals.

Unlike professional boxing, at the Games the boxers wear different coloured gloves (red or blue, to denote the corner they fight from) with a large white area, which they must use to land a scoring blow, and protective headgear. The contests are limited to a maximum of three rounds of three minutes.

Disputed decisions

Disputed decisions are the usual cause of controversy in boxing at the Olympic Games. In 1964, a Spaniard was suspended for life, having attacked the referee after being disqualified, and a South Korean refused to leave the ring for nearly an hour after being disqualified.

In 1984 in Los Angeles, where the United States won nine gold medals – it was claimed that referees and judges were intimidated by fanatically partisan American crowds. The South Koreans were particularly upset, and this was to have a backlash effect at the next Games, in Seoul, where matters came to a head.

First, a South Korean boxing official attacked a referee in the ring when the verdict went

IRISH EYES ARE SMILING Michael Carruth (IRL) won the welterweight gold medal at Barcelona

Boxing at Barcelona **The familiar red and blue face each other in an early bout**

against a home fighter, who staged a record sit-in, spending the next 70 minutes in the ring. Then light middleweight Park Si-Hun (KOR), was given a 3–2 verdict over Roy Jones (USA) despite being clearly outpunched. Jones, however, won the Val Barker Trophy, awarded to the best technical boxer at each Olympic Games.

Computer scoring

Something had to be done, and a new computer-based scoring system was first used in the Olympic Games in 1992.

Each judge has one second to record a scoring punch by pressing a red or blue button, and one point is registered for the boxer concerned if at least three of the five judges record the punch. The computer is linked up to a scoreboard above the ring, so that everyone in the arena can see the running total of each boxer and the result is known as soon as the bout is over. If the referee has cause to issue a warning to a boxer, the computer is switched to another mode and a red light shows on the judges' monitors, giving them three seconds to register the deduction of a point.

As a backstop to the new system, a jury of five members of the world governing body sit at each bout and make their own scoring decisions on paper. This is used not only in case the computer breaks down, but also to monitor the performances of the judges.

The computerized scoring system has brought a much-needed openness to boxing contests, but teething problems were evident at Barcelona. This was apparent when light flyweight Rafael Lozano (ESP) won a 6–5 second-round verdict over Eric Griffin (USA) even though he was clearly outpunched. Griffin landed at least five punches to Lozano's head near the end of round two, for which the referee gave him a standing eight count, but no scoring blows were registered to Griffin. A US protest failed.

In with a fighting chance

Boxing gold medals have been shared out all around the world. The dominant nation at present is Cuba, who collected seven gold and two silver medals in 1992. They are likely to provide the main medal threats at every weight in Atlanta, although the USA should do significantly better than their low of just one gold in Barcelona.

MEDALS TABLE

LIGHT FLYWEIGHT		
1		
2		
3		

FLYWEIGHT		
1		
2		
3		

BANTAMWEIGHT		
1		
2		
3		

FEATHERWEIGHT		
1		
2		
3		

LIGHTWEIGHT		
1		
2		
3		

LIGHT WELTERWEIGHT		
1		
2		
3		

WELTERWEIGHT		
1		
2		
3		

LIGHT MIDDLEWEIGHT		
1		
2		
3		

MIDDLEWEIGHT		
1		
2		
3		

LIGHT HEAVYWEIGHT		
1		
2		
3		

HEAVYWEIGHT		
1		
2		
3		

SUPER HEAVYWEIGHT		
1		
2		
3		

JUDO

It was a proud moment for Japan when judo first graced the Olympic Games in 1964 at Tokyo. But a giant Dutchman shattered the myth of Japanese invincibility in the sport.

Before the 19-stone (266lb/120kg) Anton Geesink came along, the Japanese, who invented the sport, believed that it was possible for a skilled small man to compete with a skilled big man on equal terms. But the Dutchman's success in the 1961 world judo championships underlined the need for weight categories in the sport.

In the 1964 Games, there were four classes including the Open, and Japan won three of them, but not the one they really wanted – Geesink took the open class. And the next time judo was included, in the Munich Olympics in 1972, another Dutchman, Wilhelm Ruska, won not only the Open but also the over 93kg (205lb) class. It was 1976 before a Japanese, Haruki Uemura, finally won the Open category.

Form and favourites

Judo has been a regular sport at the Games since 1972, and there are now seven weight categories. Women's judo made its début in 1992, also with seven classes.

Japan continue to produce technically brilliant performers, but such is the competition from many quarters that it is unlikely they will ever dominate the sport as they once did. At Barcelona in 1992, 10 countries shared the 14 gold medals, five each in the men's and women's events. Japan won two men's golds, as did the Unified Team – including the Open category, won by David Khakhaleishvili. France and host country Spain both won two women's golds.

The story was very much the same at the 1995 World Judo Championships, held in Makuhari, Japan. There is still an Open category as well as the heavyweight – over 95kg (209lb) men, 72kg (159lb) women – in the world championships, and both men's golds were won by Barcelona bronze medallist David Douillet (FRA), with champion Khakhaleishvili (now GEO) winning a bronze in the heavyweight. Dutch competitors won the two women's golds in these events.

Other successful nations in 1995 included Japan, with two men's and one women's, South Korea (one and two), and Cuba (two women's). France also won a women's gold. The top eight in each category automatically qualify for Atlanta, and perhaps the outstanding prospect, apart from Douillet, is the brilliant light-middleweight winner, Toshihiko Koga (JAP), who is also the reigning lightweight champion.

JAPANESE GOLD Hidehiko Yoshida (78kg) in 1992

Points to success

Judo contests may be won outright by a perfect throw or a 30-second hold-down – ippon, worth 10 points. The referee may award a waza-ari, a less than perfect throw, worth 7 points, and two of these also wins the contest outright. If a contest goes its full distance (4min men, 3min women), other scores and penalties come into play.

The judo competition is run on a knock-out basis for gold and silver, but a complex repêchage system is used to determine the two bronze medallists, the two losing semi-finalists stage each meeting the winner of the repêchage from the other half of the draw.

MEDALS TABLE MEN

BANTAMWEIGHT (60kg/132lb)		
1		
2		
3		

FEATHERWEIGHT (65kg/143lb)		
1		
2		
3		

LIGHTWEIGHT (71kg/157lb)		
1		
2		
3		

LIGHT MIDDLEWEIGHT (78kg/172lb)		
1		
2		
3		

MIDDLEWEIGHT (86kg/190lb)		
1		
2		
3		

LIGHT HEAVYWEIGHT (95kg/209lb)		
1		
2		
3		

HEAVYWEIGHT (min95kg/209lb)		
1		
2		
3		

MEDALS TABLE WOMEN

BANTAMWEIGHT (48kg/106lb)		
1		
2		
3		

FEATHERWEIGHT (52kg/115lb)		
1		
2		
3		

LIGHTWEIGHT (56kg/123lb)		
1		
2		
3		

LIGHT MIDDLEWEIGHT (61kg/134lb)		
1		
2		
3		

MIDDLEWEIGHT (66kg/146lb)		
1		
2		
3		

LIGHT HEAVYWEIGHT (72kg/159lb)		
1		
2		
3		

HEAVYWEIGHT (min72kg/159lb)		
1		
2		
3		

WRESTLING

Wrestling is one of the oldest sports, and featured in the ancient Greek Olympics. The Romans developed this form of wrestling into the Greco-Roman style which has survived to the present day.

There have been wrestling events in the modern Games since 1904, and today there are two styles – Greco-Roman, in which holds below the waist are barred, and freestyle – each with 10 weight categories, for men only.

Contests and contenders

A wrestling bout lasts 5 minutes and may be won outright by pinning an opponent's shoulder-blades to the mat for a count of one or by leading by 15 points or more. The referee awards points for specific throws and moves, and these points determine the winner if the bout goes the distance. Contestants fight a series of bouts in two pools, and the leaders from each pool face each other to determine gold, silver and bronze (only one) medals and other placings.

The Unified (Soviet) Team excelled in the 1992 Olympics, winning medals in 16 of the 20 classes, including three golds in each of the two styles. The USA also won three titles in freestyle, which is practised at high school and collegiate levels.

STYLE **John Smith (USA) won the 1992 62kg class**

MEDALS TABLE FREESTYLE

LIGHT FLYWEIGHT (48kg/106lb)		
1		
2		
3		
FLYWEIGHT (52kg/115lb)		
1		
2		
3		
BANTAMWEIGHT (57kg/126lb)		
1		
2		
3		
FEATHERWEIGHT (62kg/137lb)		
1		
2		
3		
LIGHTWEIGHT (68kg/150lb)		
1		
2		
3		
WELTERWEIGHT (74kg/163lb)		
1		
2		
3		
MIDDLEWEIGHT (82kg/181lb)		
1		
2		
3		
LIGHT HEAVYWEIGHT (90kg/198lb)		
1		
2		
3		
HEAVYWEIGHT (100kg/220lb)		
1		
2		
3		
SUPER-HEAVYWEIGHT (130kg/287lb)		
1		
2		
3		

MEDALS TABLE GRECO-ROMAN

LIGHT FLYWEIGHT (48kg/106lb)		
1		
2		
3		
FLYWEIGHT (52kg/115lb)		
1		
2		
3		
BANTAMWEIGHT (57kg/126lb)		
1		
2		
3		
FEATHERWEIGHT (62kg/137lb)		
1		
2		
3		
LIGHTWEIGHT (68kg/150lb)		
1		
2		
3		
WELTERWEIGHT (74kg/163lb)		
1		
2		
3		
MIDDLEWEIGHT (82kg/181lb)		
1		
2		
3		
LIGHT HEAVYWEIGHT (90kg/198lb)		
1		
2		
3		
HEAVYWEIGHT (100kg/220lb)		
1		
2		
3		
SUPER-HEAVYWEIGHT (130kg/287lb)		
1		
2		
3		

WEIGHTLIFTING

A battle of mind over matter, weightlifting calls for concentration, technique, timing and strategy as well as sheer brute force.

Men have vied with each other over thousands of years in performing feats of strength, but it is only in this century that weightlifting emerged as an international sport. There were contests in the Games of 1896 – a one-hand lift and a two-hand lift – and, in 1904, the latter plus an event called "All-Round Dumbbell", which included nine different types of lifts. But weightlifting did not achieve a permanent place in the Games until 1920, when five weight divisions were introduced.

From 1928 to 1972, the medals were determined by the aggregate of three lifts – the press, the snatch and the clean and jerk. From 1976, the press was dropped. There are now 10 weight categories, and only men compete in the Games.

Snatch, clean and jerk

In the snatch, the lifter raises the bar above his head in one continuous movement. In the clean and jerk, there are two movements – the clean brings the bar up to the lifter's shoulders; the jerk takes the bar to arm's length over his head.

The two lifts are conducted as separate contests, and competitors are allowed three tries in each lift. They draw lots for order of appearance, but may come in at any weight. The bar's weight is increased by 2.5kg (5.5lb) after each round. A competitor may not go back to a lighter weight after a failure. He may attempt the same weight again, or go for a heavier one. But if a lifter fails with all three attempts, he is eliminated from the competition.

Three judges determine whether a lift is fair (white light comes on) or not (red light). Two lights of the same colour overrule the third light. If, when both contests are completed, two lifters register the same aggregate, the one with the lighter bodyweight takes precedence.

Honours go east

At the 1992 Olympics, the Unified (Soviet) Team won 11 medals, including five golds. Bulgaria and Poland also have good records, and China have become a force in the lighter classes. Naim Suleymanoglu (TUR) successfully defended his 1988 gold medal at Barcelona in the 64kg (141lb) category.

DOUBLE GOLD Naim Suleymanoglu (TUR) retained his 60kg Olympic title in 1992, again outclassing his rivals

MEDALS TABLE

54kg (119lb)		
1		
2		
3		

59kg (130lb)		
1		
2		
3		

64kg (141lb)		
1		
2		
3		

70kg (154lb)		
1		
2		
3		

76kg (168lb)		
1		
2		
3		

83kg (183lb)		
1		
2		
3		

91kg (201lb)		
1		
2		
3		

99kg (218lb)		
1		
2		
3		

108kg (238lb)		
1		
2		
3		

min108kg (238lb)		
1		
2		
3		

BASEBALL

Baseball is the national pastime of the USA, but Cuba have dominated the amateur game.

HITTING OUT
A Japanese batter lets fly in Barcelona. Japan beat the USA in the match for the bronze medal

Eight teams compete, playing a round-robin tournament, with the top four going through to the semi-finals.

Six times a demonstration event, baseball became a full medal sport in 1992, when Cuba duly won the gold medal. After 18–0 wins against both Italy and Spain in the round-robin stage, Cuba beat Chinese Taipei (Taiwan) 11–1 in the final. Cuba's closest match was against the USA, in the first stage, when they came from behind to win 9–6. But they beat the USA 6–1 in the semi-finals. The US team – college and high school students – were beaten 8–3 by Japan for the bronze medal, and they will need to be better prepared if they are to challenge in Atlanta.

Play ball

Baseball is a ten-a-side game – eight fielders who bat, plus the pitcher and a "designated hitter" who hits for the pitcher but does not field. Substitutions are made as required – the retiring player cannot return. Each game lasts nine innings, with three outs for each side to an inning. The object is to score runs by hitting the ball and running round the three bases and returning to home plate.

The pitcher throws the ball over a 17in (43cm), five-sided plate. A good pitch is a strike – after three strikes the batter is out – and a bad pitch is a ball – after four balls the batter goes to first base.

SOFTBALL

Softball, a scaled-down version of baseball, is Atlanta's only new sport. There are three separate codes – slow-pitch, modified fast-pitch and fast-pitch – but only fast-pitch for women will be contested in 1996.

Softball is played on a smaller diamond, with a shorter pitching distance, and is over seven innings. The ball, as the name suggests, is softer than in baseball, although it is larger and must be pitched underarm. Nevertheless, the speed of the pitch is comparable to baseball. The difference in pitching between softball and baseball is the method of delivery, which has to underarm.

The competition format is the same as for baseball. The USA will be strong favourites to win the gold medal, though Japan, Australia and Italy will all be competitive.

MEDALS TABLE

BASEBALL (MEN)		
1		
2		
3		

SOFTBALL (WOMEN)		
1		
2		
3		

FOOTBALL

After the brilliant success of the United States in hosting the 1994 World Cup, no one doubts that football will be a huge attraction in the 1996 Games. Football, the world's most popular pastime, is the fastest growing sport in the USA. And not only will their men's team go in with a chance of honours, the USA will start among the favourites to win the first ever women's football gold medal at the Olympic Games.

The only football at the first Olympic Games, in 1896 at Athens, consisted of an unofficial play-off between two Greek towns, the winners of which lost 15–0 to a Danish XI, so it is not entirely inappropriate that at the Centennial Games the football finals will take place in Athens – Athens, Georgia, that is!

Football was, however, the first team sport to be included in the Olympic Games, in Paris in 1900. With only three countries competing, Great Britain, represented by the Upton Park Football Club, beat France 4–0 to win the gold medals.

The world governing body FIFA was founded in 1904, and from 1908 the competition began to thrive. Uruguay won in 1924, and again in 1928 with nine of the team that went on to win the inaugural World Cup in 1930. The definition of the football amateur, however, caused considerable controversy, especially when Eastern Bloc countries entered and dominated the competition after World War Two.

WOMEN'S FOOTBALL The USA beat Japan 4–0 in the 1995 World Cup quarter-finals

No more amateur

With the relaxation of the amateur regulations, the 1984 football tournament at the Los Angeles Games permitted the inclusion of professionals, so long as they had not participated in the World Cup. Exceptionally big crowds watched the matches, including a US record of nearly 102,000 at the Pasadena Rose Bowl to see France beat Brazil 2–0 in the final.

Football made further inroads into the prejudices of the American media and public when the USA staged the 1994 World Cup and produced a competitive team. Law changes brought in for the 1994 World Cup were designed to reduce unnecessary delays and reward attacking play, thus making the game more attractive, and to a large extent they have been successful.

Now, at the Atlanta Olympic Games, a revolutionary communications system for match officials will be used for the first time, indeed as an experiment for major football competitions. Equipped with a transmitter, linesmen and women will be able to send an electronic signal to a receiver worn by the referee to draw the latter's attention to incidents that might otherwise result in a late call or escape his or her notice altogether.

Staging the 1996 finals

Qualification for the 16 places in men's football was arranged in continental zones, and 121 national teams vied to reach Atlanta. Only players born on or after January 1, 1973, were eligible to take part in the qualifying competition. Teams in the finals, however, will be permitted to field three players who are not subject to age or other restrictions, although the others may not have already played in the finals of an Olympic Games tournament.

In the men's finals, four groups of four will play round-robin matches, with the first two in each group going through to the knock-out stage. There are four seeded teams, the hosts USA and one representative each from Africa, Europe and South America. The eight finalists in the women's tournament will play in two groups of four, with hosts USA and World Champions Norway seeded, and the top two in each group will progress to the semi-finals.

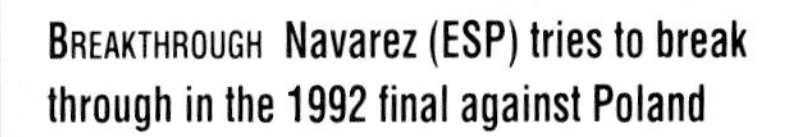
BREAKTHROUGH Navarez (ESP) tries to break through in the 1992 final against Poland

HOME WIN The Spanish side who beat Poland 3–2 to win football gold medals in Barcelona

Athens to host finals

All group matches will be played at four venues: Legion Field, Birmingham, Alabama; the Orlando Citrus Bowl, Florida; the Orange Bowl Stadium, Miami; and the Robert F. Kennedy Memorial Stadium, Washington, D.C. All matches from the semi-finals will be played at the 84,000-seat Sanford Stadium, on the campus of the University of Georgia, in Athens, Georgia.

The United States, encouraged by the performance of their 1994 World Cup team, who were beaten only 1-0 in the last 16 by eventual winners Brazil, must be contenders for honours in 1996, with their own crowds behind them again. Other contenders will emerge not only from the strong European and South American qualifying groups, but also from Africa, whose leading footballing nations are becoming increasingly powerful, especially at youth level.

Winners of the first Women's World Championships in 1991 and third in China in 1995, the United States have a strong women's squad, while other powers include Norway, Sweden, Germany and China.

MEDALS TABLE MEN

FOOTBALL

1		
2		
3		

MEDALS TABLE WOMEN

FOOTBALL

1		
2		
3		

HOCKEY

Among the fastest ball games in the world, hockey is a fine spectacle. The great Indian players of the twenties and thirties are said to have held crowds spellbound at the mastery of their stickwork.

Hockey is played with 11 players per side, over two periods of 35 minutes. Players may strike the ball with the front face of the stick only, and may score goals only from within the shooting, or striking, circle (in reality, a flattened semi-circle).

In the men's tournament, the leading two of each round-robin pool of six nations go through to the semi-finals. The women's format has been changed for Atlanta, eight teams now playing in one pool instead of two.

India leads the way

Men's hockey made its first appearance in the Games in 1908, but did not become a regular sport until 1928, when India began one of the longest winning streaks in Games history. They won that tournament without conceding a goal in their five matches, and proceeded to win the next five hockey gold medals, too.

Until they were beaten 1-0 by Pakistan in the 1960 final, they won all 30 of their matches and never conceded more than one goal in a game. The subcontinent continued to dominate the hockey tournaments until West Germany beat Pakistan 1–0 in the ill-tempered final of 1972.

While India and Pakistan will always produce teams to challenge for the medals, the competition is much fiercer now, and several other countries, such as Germany and Australia, are also capable of taking the honours.

The women's game

With the emphasis on sportsmanship rather than international competition, women's hockey did not make the Olympic Games until 1980 at Moscow, and then five of the six countries scheduled to compete withdrew as part of the political boycott. Zimbabwe, invited to play only five weeks before the Games, won the gold.

No country has won the women's gold medal more than once. The Netherlands, champions in 1984, have been exceptionally successful in the World Cup and other major international championships, but only just managed to qualify for Atlanta on goal difference in a group led by South Korea and Britain.

MEDALS TABLE MEN

HOCKEY		
1		
2		
3		

MEDALS TABLE WOMEN

HOCKEY		
1		
2		
3		

GRIM DEFENCE The German women won the silver medals in 1992, their men won the golds

HANDBALL

MEDALS TABLE MEN

HANDBALL	
1	
2	
3	

MEDALS TABLE WOMEN

HANDBALL	
1	
2	
3	

One of the features of team handball is the acrobatics required of the goalkeepers to defend their net. Opposing players can pick their spot for goalbound efforts and, unlike soccer, outside conditions cannot affect the ball's flight in the indoor court.

This fast-paced, all-action sport is like basketball with soccer-style goals. The tactics are similar in that teams move the ball upcourt towards their opponents' goal by dribbling and passing. But once within shooting distance, instead of the precise lob or high leap to place the ball in a hanging basket, handball attackers wind their body up like a coiled spring before hurling the ball at the target.

The handball court measures 40m by 20m (44yd by 22yd) and the goals are 3m (10ft) wide and 2m (6.5ft) high. The game is played seven-a-side, with five substitutes who may be interchanged at any time, and there are two 30min periods, 20min for women. The ball, smaller than a soccer ball, measures 58–60cm (23–24in) circumference for men, 54–56cm (21–22in) for women.

Only the goalkeeper is allowed inside the goal area, so the closest shooting distance is 6m (6.5yd) out from goal. Except for a goalkeeper blocking a shot, players may not touch the ball with their foot or any part of the leg below the knee. They may not take more than three steps with the ball without bouncing it. Once players catch the ball, they are allowed three steps and three seconds before releasing it.

Metamorphosis of a sport

Handball in its present form has been played for little more than 40 years. It was invented in Europe in the 1890s, and before World War Two was played 11-a-side, out-of-doors on a soccer-type pitch. This version figured in the 1936 Olympic Games in Berlin, but it was only when the number of players was reduced from 11 to 7 in 1952 that its popularity soared.

In the Atlanta tournaments, the top two teams in each of two round-robin groups of six (four for women) qualify for the semi-finals. The sport has been largely dominated by eastern European nations in major competitions, with the chief exception of South Korea, whose women have won the last two titles and whose men took the silver medals in 1988.

FINAL WIND-UP
Sung-ok Oh (KOR) winds up to for a shot at goal in the 1992 final – Korea beat Norway 25–21

TENNIS

Because of the traditional importance of the Grand Slam championships and the enormous amounts of money at stake in grand prix events, tennis has not quite taken off at the Games since its 1988 revival. But with more of the top players expected to take part, and the increasing pride in playing for country rather than cash, tennis in Atlanta is likely to be a top event.

Tennis featured in the Olympic Games from 1896 until 1924. It was a tennis player who had the honour of being the first woman to win an Olympic Games gold medal, Charlotte Cooper (GBR), in 1900. There was a mixed doubles event in 1900 and from 1912 to 1924. Women's doubles was not included until 1920.

Normal service returns

Reappearing first as a demonstration event in the 1984 Games, tennis became a full medal sport again at Seoul, in 1988, but with no mixed doubles. Tennis at the Games is played like any other major tournament – 64 players in the singles and 32 pairs in the doubles – as a straight knock-out, with 16 seeds in singles (both men and women) and eight in doubles.

For Atlanta, there will be no qualifying events, and participation will be based on computer rankings or wild card entry; only the men's finals will be best-of-five sets (instead of all men's matches); and there will be a bronze-medal match instead of awarding bronze to both losing semi-finalists.

Courting favour

Spectators in Stone Mountain Park, where a complex of more than 10 courts has been specially constructed for the Games, can expect to see the world's leading players battling it out for the medals on Centre Court – Pete Sampras (USA), Andre Agassi (USA), Boris Becker (GER) featuring in the men's, and perhaps Monica Seles (USA) will continue her exciting comeback from her traumatic injury to challenge Steffi Graf (GER) for the women's gold. The hard, fast Plexipave surface will favour big servers such as defending champion Marc Rosset (SUI) and Goran Ivanisevic (CRO), and no woman will feel safe against the likes of Mariaan De Swardt (RSA).

MEDALS TABLE MEN

SINGLES		
1		
2		
3		

DOUBLES		
1		
2		
3		

MEDALS TABLE WOMEN

SINGLES		
1		
2		
3		

DOUBLES		
1		
2		
3		

STEFFI GRAF (GER), 1988 WOMEN'S SINGLES CHAMPION, WILL BE KEEN TO MAKE AMENDS FOR THE LOSS OF HER TITLE IN THE LAST GAMES TO JENNIFER CAPRIATI (USA). FITNESS PROBLEMS HAVE BESET GRAF IN RECENT YEARS, AND FOOT SURGERY KEPT HER OUT OF THE 1996 AUSTRALIAN OPEN, WON BY HER CO-LEADER IN THE WORLD RANKINGS, MONICA SELES. BUT THE SIX-TIMES WIMBLEDON SINGLES CHAMPION HAS THE EXPERIENCE, THE COURT CRAFT AND THE DETERMINATION TO TRIUMPH IN ATLANTA.

BADMINTON

Badminton made its debut as a medal sport at Barcelona in 1992. The indoor sport has a fanatical following in the Orient, an area which has enjoyed the most success in international competition.

Badminton is conducted on a straight knock-out basis from the start, with 64 entrants in singles (eight seeds) and 32 in doubles (four seeds), and both losing semi-finalists winning bronze. All matches are best-of-three sets, 15 points per set, except women's singles, which are 11-up. Only the server can score points. If the receiver wins a rally, service changes.

The first champions

The badminton tournament, in Barcelona, was a triumph for Indonesia, who won their first ever Olympic Games gold medals, their players taking both singles titles. Susi Susanti won the women's singles, and her long-time boyfriend Allan Kusuma won the men's.

Mixed doubles have been added for Atlanta, and this will give the Europeans, especially Denmark, golden chances. Thomas Lund and Marlene Thomsen (DEN) beat another Danish pair in the 1995 World Championships final, but most of the other medals went to the Orient – to Indonesia, South Korea and China. Susanti lost her world title to eventual winner Ye Zhaoying (CHN) in the semi-finals.

MEDALS TABLE MEN

SINGLES		
1		
2		
3		

DOUBLES		
1		
2		
3		

MIXED DOUBLES		
1		
2		
3		

MEDALS TABLE WOMEN

SINGLES		
1		
2		
3		

DOUBLES		
1		
2		
3		

TABLE TENNIS

China has been the dominant table tennis nation in recent times and when the sport became a part of the Games, in 1992, their players won all but one gold medal. China won all seven competitions at the 1995 World Championships.

There are men's and women's singles and doubles – no mixed doubles. In all the events, 32 competitors or pairs are divided into eight round-robin groups, playing each other in best-of-three matches, the eight winners going through to the knock-out stage, in which matches are all best-of-five games. Both losing semi-finalists win bronze medals.

Rivals to China

The biggest danger to the Chinese players in Atlanta will probably come from Europe and Korea. Jan Waldner (SWE) beat Jean Gatien (FRA) in the 1992 singles final and a German pair won silver in the men's doubles, with Koreans taking both bronze medals.

The 1992 gold medallist, Deng Yaping (CHN), needed five sets in the World Championship final to overcome her doubles partner in Barcelona, Qiao Hong, to confirm her top rank.

MEDALS TABLE MEN

SINGLES		
1		
2		
3		

DOUBLES		
1		
2		
3		

MEDALS TABLE WOMEN

SINGLES		
1		
2		
3		

DOUBLES		
1		
2		
3		

BASKETBALL

Basketball is one of the world's most exciting indoor sports and, with only a basket nailed to a wall and a large ball needed, one of the easiest to play. The basic rules are equally simple: no running with the ball – except when dribbling – only the hands to be used for passing and no deliberate physical contact.

HAKEEM OLAJUWON (USA), THE HOUSTON ROCKETS' VETERAN 2.12M (7FT) CENTRE, PLAYED FOR NIGERIA IN 1980 IN THE AFRICAN JUNIOR CHAMPIONSHIPS, BUT, HAVING GAINED US CITIZENSHIP IN 1993, HAS BEEN CLEARED – AND CHOSEN – TO REPRESENT THE US 'DREAM TEAM III' IN ATLANTA. WITH THE ROCKETS SINCE 1985, HE WAS VOTED LEAGUE MVP IN 1994, WHEN HE LED HOUSTON TO THE NBA TITLE AND MADE THE ALL-NBA TEAM FOR THE FIFTH TIME.

A YMCA training school instructor at Springfield, Massachusetts, Dr James Naismith devised basketball in 1891 as an indoor game to keep students occupied when it was not possible to play sport outside in the frozen New England winter. He hung peach baskets from the balcony at opposite ends of the gymnasium – hence the name of the game.

Basketball is an end-to-end game, with frequent goals, or baskets, each basket being attacked in turn. A goal from open play is worth 2 points, or, if the shot is made from outside a marked semi-circle, 3 points. Free throws, which are awarded for various offences, are worth 1 point each. Depending on the nature and situation of the offence, one, two or three free throws are awarded.

The game caught on quickly in North America and then internationally, and 21 nations sent teams to the 1936 Games. After World War Two, basketball's popularity grew even more rapidly, and there are now 193 countries affiliated to FIBA, the world's governing body.

Close encounters

In 1996, there will be 12 countries contesting the men's and women's finals, and they are split into two round-robin groups, with the top four in each going through to knock-out quarter-finals.

Basketball has been an Olympic Games sport since 1936 – 1976 for women. The 1972 USA–USSR final has gone down in history as one of the most sensational matches of all time in any sport. But no team has caused such anticipation as the American 'Dream Team' in Barcelona. This collection of sporting millionaires, the cream of the professional ranks, did not let their fans down, and now more thrills are expected in Atlanta from Dream Team III – Dream Team II cleaned up in the 1994 World Championships.

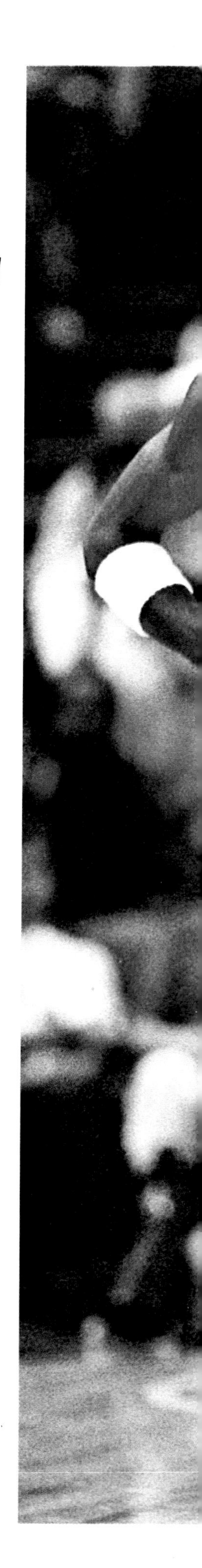

PLAY IT AGAIN UNCLE SAM

THE 1972 BASKETBALL FINAL BETWEEN THE USA AND THE SOVIET UNION WAS STRAIGHT OUT OF SCHOOLBOY FICTION. NEVER BEATEN IN ANY OF THE TEAM'S 63 BASKETBALL GAMES, THE US TEAM – THE CREAM OF THE NATION'S COLLEGIATE TALENT – WAS STRUGGLING AGAINST THE POWERFUL SOVIET SIDE BUT CREPT UP TO WITHIN A POINT WITH ONLY SECONDS TO GO.

THE SOVIETS MISSED A BASKET AND DOUG COLLINS RACED THE LENGTH OF THE COURT BEFORE BEING SENT SPRAWLING. HE DRAMATICALLY CONVERTED THE TWO FREE THROWS – USA 50, USSR 49. PLAY RESTARTED AND THE BUZZER WENT, BUT THERE WAS STILL ONE SECOND ON THE CLOCK. THE REFEREE ORDERED THIS FINAL TICK TO BE PLAYED, AND WHEN THE BUZZER SOUNDED AGAIN, THE COURT BECAME A MASS OF JUBILANT FANS AND PLAYERS.

BUT PERSISTENT LOUDSPEAKER APPEALS FINALLY GOT THE COURT CLEARED BECAUSE, APPARENTLY AND INEXPLICABLY, THE LAST THREE SECONDS HAD TO BE REPLAYED. THE AMERICANS COULD BARELY COMPREHEND THE SITUATION, AS FROM UNDER HIS OWN BASKET IVAN EDESHKO UNLEASHED A COURT-LENGTH PASS TO ALEXANDER BELOV. THE TALL RUSSIAN CAUGHT IT AND, WITH THE TWO AMERICANS GUARDING HIM HELPLESS TO INTERVENE, LEAPT UP TO SCORE THE WINNING POINTS – USSR 51, USA 50 – AS THE BUZZER WENT FOR THE LAST TIME.

DREAM TEAM
The Chicago Bulls forward Scottie Pippen, one of the most versatile players in the game, was an early choice for the US Dream Team III to play in Atlanta

The Dream Teams

The USA have been beaten only twice in men's basketball, both times by the USSR. They lost in the 1972 final and again in the 1988 semi-finals. When basketball went "open", the USA assembled a collection of stars from the ranks of the pro NBA league for the 1992 Games, players such as Michael Jordan and "Magic" Johnson, earning millions of dollars a year, and they duly swept through to the gold medals.

Players selected for the 1996 Dream Team include the likes of centres Shaquille O'Neal and Hakeem Olajuwon, forward Scottie Pippen and guard Reggie Miller, who will be playing in his third Games. Reggie's sister Cheryl won a gold with the 1984 women's team. It is difficult to see them getting beaten. Croatia – silver medallists in 1992 – are most likely to be among the challengers again.

Winners of the women's basketball title in 1984 and 1988, the USA were beaten by the Unified Team in Barcelona. Led by three-time Olympian and double gold-medallist Teresa Edwards and strengthened by their newest star, 6ft 5in (1.96m) Lisa Leslie, they will be fighting to regain their crown, with Russia and Brazil among those expected to ensure a closely fought competition.

MEDALS TABLE MEN

BASKETBALL		
1		
2		
3		

MEDALS TABLE WOMEN

BASKETBALL		
1		
2		
3		

VOLLEYBALL

Like basketball, volleyball was invented in the United States by a YMCA instructor in the 1890s (in 1895 by William Morgan). Beach volleyball, too, popular in southern California for decades, is now booming around the world, and will make its Games début at Atlanta in 1996.

CUBA CHAMPIONS Cuba beat the Unified Team in 1992 to win the women's volleyball gold medals

Both indoor and beach volleyball are played by men and women and the only difference between the two sports is that the game under the bright sun and on the stamina-sapping soft sand contains two players per side, while the original version has six per side.

Dig, set and spike

The object of the game is to score points by grounding the ball in the opposing court or forcing your opponents into an error. Service is from an area behind the back line of each court. At the start of each service, the players of each side must line up with three players in front of the attack line, marked 3m (10ft) from the net, and three behind it.

When the ball crosses the net, the opposing team has three touches (with hand or arm) in which to return it. It may be returned on the first or second contact, but mostly a side will use the first two touches to "dig" the ball out and "set" it up for a player at the net to "spike" it downwards into the opponents' court. Only the side serving can score points. When a side wins service, their players must rotate (clockwise) their starting positions. The best of five 15-point sets is played in the Olympic Games.

MEDALS TABLE MEN

INDOOR

1		
2		
3		

BEACH

1		
2		
3		

MEDALS TABLE WOMEN

INDOOR

1		
2		
3		

BEACH

1		
2		
3		

Women's teams have been increased from eight to 12 for Atlanta, matching the size of the men's competition. The top four of two round-robin groups go through to knock-out quarter-finals. The losing semi-finalists play off for the bronze medal.

Favourites on court and beach

Both men's and women's volleyball were admitted to the Games in 1964, and were dominated largely by the USSR, and to a lesser extent by Japan, until the early eighties. Since then, the USA have enjoyed much success in men's volleyball, although 1994 world champions Italy put themselves in the driving seat for 1996 by winning the pre-Games event at Atlanta, the Centennial Cup, in August 1995, accounting for the USA in a five-setter before beating Barcelona champions Brazil in the final.

Holders Cuba will probably start favourites to win the women's volleyball in Atlanta, but home advantage should put the US team in contention.

With crucially more experience in the game, the USA will be favourites for both gold medals at stake on Atlanta Beach.

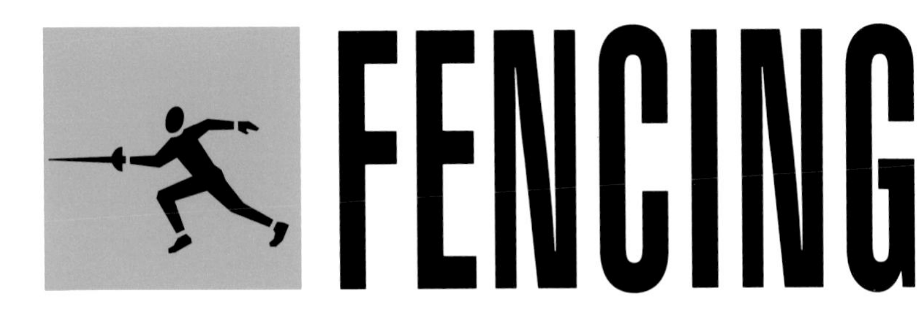

FENCING

Fencing has been likened to a game of chess played at lightning speed. Fencers have to plan all the time, often several moves ahead, analysing their opponents' moves, thinking always of how to outwit them.

Sword-fighting is an age-old pastime as well as a means of waging war, and fencing was one of the original sports in the first of the modern Games, with individual men's events for foil and sabre. The épée followed in 1900, and by 1908 there were team events for all three weapons.

Women's fencing made its first appearance on the piste with the individual foil in 1924, the team event following in 1960. In Atlanta, women move closer to parity with men with the addition of individual and team épée events.

Weapons and target areas

Scoring in fencing is by "hits", touching your opponent with the weapon. The foil and the heavier épée are thrusting weapons, and scoring hits may be made only with the point of the sword. The sabre is a cut-and-thrust weapon, hits being scored with the whole of the front edge and the top third of the back edge.

The target area for the foil is the chest only, for the sabre the whole upper body, including arms and head – in both, hits must follow special movements – and for the épée, the "duelling" sword, the whole body, including limbs and head. Fencers wear protective clothing and a wire-mesh face mask. They are wired up so that hits may be recorded electronically and signalled by a system of lights on the judges' table.

Contests and contenders

Contests are determined on the best of three, first-to-five bouts (or the first to six hits if the score reaches 4–4). Some fencers are eliminated after a series of preliminary contests, and then there are several repêchage rounds before the last eight emerge into a straight knock-out tournament from the quarter-finals. There is also a bronze medal play-off.

Italy and France are traditionally the leading nations in men's foil and épée, while Hungarians have excelled in the sabre. Soviet women have a good record in foil and sabre, but are no longer the dominant force they once were. Italy won the 1992 women's team foil title inspired by the individual gold-medallist Giovanna Trillini, whose aggressive swordplay was a feature of the fencing hall in Barcelona.

FOILED AGAIN Women's fencing in Barcelona produced a popular winner in the Italian Giovanna Trillini (right)

MEDALS TABLE MEN

FOIL INDIVIDUAL		
1		
2		
3		

FOIL TEAM		
1		
2		
3		

EPEE INDIVIDUAL		
1		
2		
3		

EPEE TEAM		
1		
2		
3		

SABRE INDIVIDUAL		
1		
2		
3		

SABRE TEAM		
1		
2		
3		

MEDALS TABLE WOMEN

FOIL INDIVIDUAL		
1		
2		
3		

FOIL TEAM		
1		
2		
3		

EPEE INDIVIDUAL		
1		
2		
3		

EPEE TEAM		
1		
2		
3		

CYCLING

LAST-LAP LUNGE
In the track sprint, riders do not go all out until the last of the four laps

The exciting sport of mountain bike racing, only 10 years old but increasingly popular, joins the other two major cycling disciplines, road racing and track racing, and completes a highly diversified cycling programme.

Cycling at the 1996 Centennial Games receives two shots in the arm at Atlanta, not only with the inclusion of mountain-bike racing – for women as well as men – but the other two disciplines have been made even more competitive with the acceptance of professional cyclists.

Pros and cons of the road

Olympic Games cycling has followed in the footsteps of sports such as tennis and basketball and gone "open". Road racing in particular has long been a stepping-stone for amateurs intending to turn professional, and gold-medallists have in general made the transition so swiftly that no individual rider has successfully defended a road race title. Now that turning pro is no longer a disbarment from the Olympic Games, title-holders are more likely to compete again. But, tragically, the 1992 men's champion, Fabio Casartelli (ITA), was killed in a high-speed crash during the 1995 Tour de France.

Tough schedule for Atlanta

However, the famous Tour is by far the most important event in the professional calender and, with the 1996 race finishing only 10 days before the Olympic Games road race, and a mere 13 days before the time trial, it remains to be seen whether any of the top riders will compete in Atlanta.

The leading contenders would include time-triallist supreme Miguel Indurain (ESP), who joined the cycling "immortals" when he won his fifth successive Tour de France in 1995, and Chris Boardman (GBR), who turned pro after his 1992 track triumph in Barcelona, but sensationally crashed out of the Tour in the Prologue and was out of action for several months.

Trial of strength

Some changes have been made in the road cycling programme for Atlanta. The men's team time trial, held since 1960, has been dropped, but both men's and women's individual time trials are included for the first time. A men's individual road race was staged at the first modern Games, in 1896, and has been held regularly since 1912.

Women did not compete in cycle racing at the Games until 1984, when an individual road race was included. The 1988 winner, Dutch rider Monique Knol, went close to retaining her title in Barcelona, but had to be content with a bronze, less than 2 seconds behind gold-medallist Kathy Watt (AUS) after more than 2 hours of cycling.

CHRIS BOARDMAN (GBR) CAUSED A SENSATION IN BARCELONA WITH HIS HIGH-TECH LOTUS BIKE IN THE 4,000M PURSUIT EVENT. HE TWICE BROKE THE WORLD RECORD IN THE HEATS, AND IN THE FINAL EASILY ACCOUNTED FOR WORLD CHAMPION JENS LEHMANN (GER), WHO GRACEFULLY ACKNOWLEDGED THAT IT WAS THE MAN WHO BEAT HIM AND NOT THE MACHINE. TURNING PRO, BOARDMAN SHOWED GREAT POTENTIAL IN THE VERY DIFFERENT WORLD OF ROAD RACING.

MEDALS TABLE WOMEN

102km ROAD RACE

1		
2		
3		

26km TIME TRIAL

1		
2		
3		

SPRINT

1		
2		
3		

3,000m PURSUIT

1		
2		
3		

30km POINTS RACE

1		
2		
3		

MOUNTAIN BIKE RACE

1		
2		
3		

Banking on gold

Four different types of races take place on the banked, 250m cycle track.

In the sprints, over 1000m for both men and women, riders spend the greater part of the race jockeying for position and trying to slipstream opponents before making a final dash for the line. Times given are for the last 200m. A maximum of four riders take part in each heat, and there are repêchages in the early rounds. The quarter-finals onwards are best-of-three races, and only two riders take part.

The only time trial on the track is a men's 1000m, in which each rider races separately. In pursuit, two riders or teams start on opposite sides of the track, and the race is decided on time or if one rider or team catches the other.

In points races – the women's making its début in Atlanta – points are awarded for the first four (5-3-2-1) across the line after every 1500m (6 laps), with double points at the finish. Positions are decided on points scored, but riders who do not finish are eliminated.

MEDALS TABLE MEN

220km ROAD RACE

1		
2		
3		

52km TIME TRIAL

1		
2		
3		

SPRINT

1		
2		
3		

1km TIME TRIAL

1		
2		
3		

4,000m PURSUIT

1		
2		
3		

4,000m TEAM PURSUIT

1		
2		
3		

50km POINTS RACE

1		
2		
3		

MOUNTAIN BIKE RACE

1		
2		
3		

Coming round the mountain

Fifty men and 30 women will contest the two mountain-biking events on a 12km course, through bumpy woodland and rolling rocky hills.

This cycling discipline, new to the Olympic Games, calls for strength, endurance and mental toughness. Invented in the eighties on the trails of Marin County, California, mountain bike racing was initially dominated by US riders, but some of the strongest challengers at the Games will come from Canada and Western Europe.

ARCHERY

Modern archery is a far cry from the bows and arrows of ancient warfare. With high-tech weapons, electronic scoring and arrows rocketing at speeds of more than 200 kilometres (125 miles) per hour – at targets the size of a tennis ball – the action is fast and furious.

Men's and women's competitions at Atlanta have each been restricted to 64 archers, which will be reduced to 32 by an open round. Then the competition becomes a straight knock-out, a system introduced in 1988 at Seoul.

Scores from the open round determine the countries that go forward to the team competition, which will have a qualifying round – if necessary – before the knock-out stage.

The advancing enemy

A round of arrows comprises 12 shots, and in the open rounds archers fire three rounds at each of four target distances: 90m (98.5yd), 70m (76.5yd), 50m (54.5yd) and 30m (33yd) for men – 70m, 60m (65.5yd), 50m and 30m for women.

Targets have a gold circle at the centre, surrounded by rings of red, blue, black and white. Each colour is divided into an inner and an outer, and arrows score from 10pts for the inner gold to 1pt for the outer white.

Whereas placings in competition were once determined by the aggregate score of 288 arrows, in the knock-out system, head-to-head matches are decided on just one round of 12 arrows from 70m, and the medallists will have played five such matches. These short, head-to-head battles are breathtakingly tense.

Archery makes a comeback

Archery competitions for men first appeared in the 1900 Games, for women four years later. After 1920, however, the sport was dropped from the programme.

Since the return of archery in 1972, Americans have won four of the five individual men's gold medals open to them. They also won the first two women's titles, but women's archery has been dominated since 1984 by South Korea, who in 1988 at Seoul produced all three medallists – aged 17, 18 and 17! This trio also won the newly instituted team-of-three title, and the Korean men's team also won the gold medals in their events. The South Koreans, whose women ruled again in 1992, will be strongly fancied again in Atlanta.

MEDALS TABLE MEN

INDIVIDUAL		
1		
2		
3		

TEAM		
1		
2		
3		

MEDALS TABLE WOMEN

INDIVIDUAL		
1		
2		
3		

TEAM		
1		
2		
3		

MODERN PENTATHLON

The modern pentathlon has its origins in military legend – a courier riding through enemy country, beating off attackers with sword and pistol before swimming across rivers and running through rough terrain to deliver his message.

The individual modern pentathlon has been in the Games since 1912, with a team event added in 1952. But for Atlanta the team event has been dropped, individual competitors cut by 56 to 32, and all five events will take place in a single day. Athletes will accumulate points in 10m air pistol, épée (round-robin, single-hit bouts), 300m freestyle swimming and riding (450m obstacle course with mounts allotted at random), before setting off at intervals (according to their totals) in the 4km cross-country run, so that the first home is the winner.

MEDALS TABLE

MODERN PENTATHLON		
1		
2		
3		

SHOOTING

The first gold medal in the 1996 Games will be awarded in shooting. There are four disciplines on the shooting ranges – rifle, pistol, running target and clay target – and some 430 marksmen and women will be chasing 15 gold medals.

Shooting was one of the original sports in the 1896 Games, perhaps because Baron Pierre de Coubertin, the founder of the modern Games, was a shooting enthusiast.

Women first competed in the shooting at Mexico City in 1968, but only against men in open events. The nearest a woman came to winning gold in these events was when Margaret Murdock (USA) tied for first place in the 1976 three-positions rifle event, but lost on a count-back over the last 10 shots. Women only shooting events were not included in the programme until 1984.

Since 1984, China – both men and women – have become the most potent force in shooting events, taking over from Europe and the USA.

ZHANG SHAN (CHN) BECAME THE FIRST WOMAN TO WIN AN OPEN SHOOTING GOLD MEDAL – IN THE SKEET – WHEN SHE DEFEATED 54 MEN IN THE 60-STRONG FIELD AT BARCELONA. SHE WILL PROBABLY BE THE LAST, TOO, AS MIXED EVENTS HAVE BEEN DROPPED BECAUSE SO FEW WOMEN QUALIFIED.

KNOWN AS "LITTLE MISS PERFECT" AT HOME, ZHANG "KILLED" A MAXIMUM 200 BIRDS IN THE PRELIMINARY ROUNDS AND SHOT A GAMES RECORD 223 OUT OF 225 OVERALL.

MEDALS TABLE WOMEN

SPORT PISTOL

1		
2		
3		

SMALL BORE RIFLE – 3 POSITIONS

1		
2		
3		

DOUBLE TRAP

1		
2		
3		

AIR PISTOL

1		
2		
3		

AIR RIFLE

1		
2		
3		

MEDALS TABLE MEN

FREE PISTOL

1		
2		
3		

RAPID-FIRE PISTOL

1		
2		
3		

SMALL BORE RIFLE – PRONE

1		
2		
3		

SMALL BORE RIFLE – 3 POSITIONS

1		
2		
3		

RUNNING GAME TARGET

1		
2		
3		

TRAP SHOOTING

1		
2		
3		

SKEET SHOOTING

1		
2		
3		

DOUBLE TRAP

1		
2		
3		

AIR PISTOL

1		
2		
3		

AIR RIFLE

1		
2		
3		

ROWING

Rowing, with cycling, is third only to athletics and swimming in the number of competitors at the Games. The 600 rowers in Atlanta will be among the Games' best-conditioned competitors and many will be seen in a state of near collapse across their oars at the end of races.

STEVE REDGRAVE (GBR) IS ONE OF SEVEN OARSMEN WHO HAVE WON THREE GOLD MEDALS, SUCCEEDING IN THE COXED FOURS IN 1984 AND THE COXLESS PAIRS, WITH DIFFERENT PARTNERS, IN 1988 AND 1992. IF HE GETS TO ATLANTA, ALL EYES WILL BE ON HIM TO SEE WHETHER HE CAN CREATE ROWING HISTORY WITH A FOURTH GOLD.

Rowing calls for intense physical and mental discipline, and nearly all the muscles are used during each stroke. Strictly, rowing is performed with one long oar held by two hands, sculling with a smaller oar, or scull, in each hand.

GOLD RUSH **Canada win the eights again in 1992**

The rowing events

By the 1924 Games, there were seven men's rowing events – single sculls, double sculls, coxed pairs, fours and eights and coxless pairs and fours. The coxless quadruple sculls was added in 1976, the same year that women's rowing made its Games début with six events – single, double and coxed quadruple sculls (coxless from 1988), coxless pairs, coxed fours (coxless from 1992) and eights.

The course – 2,000m for men and 1000m for women – has six lanes and each event is divided into heats, followed by repêchages, semi-finals and finals.

For Atlanta there has been a major change, with lightweight categories – originally introduced to attract wider participation (the first lightweight world championships were in 1974) – replacing three of the traditional events.

Strongholds of rowing

The USA dominated the men's eights up to 1956, winning gold 10 times. East German rowers were outstanding, particularly in the women's events and, unified, Germany won two men's and two women's events in Barcelona. Canadian women were sensationally successful, winning the eights and two other golds, while Romania won the single sculls gold medal for the third time in four Games.

MEDALS TABLE WOMEN

SINGLE SCULLS		
1		
2		
3		

DOUBLE SCULLS		
1		
2		
3		

COXLESS PAIRS		
1		
2		
3		

QUADRUPLE SCULLS		
1		
2		
3		

EIGHTS		
1		
2		
3		

LIGHTWEIGHT DOUBLE SCULLS		
1		
2		
3		

MEDALS TABLE MEN

SINGLE SCULLS		
1		
2		
3		

DOUBLE SCULLS		
1		
2		
3		

COXLESS PAIRS		
1		
2		
3		

COXLESS FOURS		
1		
2		
3		

QUADRUPLE SCULLS		
1		
2		
3		

EIGHTS		
2		
3		

LIGHTWEIGHT DOUBLE SCULLS		
1		
2		
3		

LIGHTWEIGHT COXLESS FOURS		
1		
2		
3		

CANOEING

WHITEWATER The spectacular C2 slalom

The two main canoe disciplines, encompassing 16 events and nearly 500 competitors, provide contrasting thrills – the sprint has tight finishes while the slalom provides a spectacular battle against nature.

In 1996, the events will have magnificent settings, Lake Lanier for still-water racing and Tennessee's Cherokee National Forest for whitewater.

There are two types of craft in canoeing – the kayak (K) and the Canadian canoe (C). They are propelled by one, two or four canoeists. The kayaker sits inside the craft, with legs outstretched under the deck, and uses a paddle with a blade at each end. In a Canadian canoe, the canoeist sits or kneels and uses a one-bladed paddle.

Back to its origins

Canoeing will be going back to the land of its origins for the 1996 Games, canoes and kayaks having been invented, it is claimed, by American Indians and Eskimos. Canoeing as a sport began in Scotland in the 1860s, when John MacGregor designed the "Rob Roy" canoe, which could be paddled and sailed.

Canoe racing for men appeared in the Games for the first time in 1936 with kayak and Canadian events over 1000m and 10km, and in 1948 a women's 500m race was added. The longer races have since been dropped, and men now race over 500m and 1000m, women over 500m in kayaks only.

As with the rowing events, only one entrant per country is permitted per event. Normally, six to eight canoes take part in heats and repêchages to produce two nine-boat semi-finals with the first four and fastest fifth contesting the final.

European countries dominate still-water canoeing, with the occasional intervention of North America or the Antipodes. In 1992, Germany won four of the nine men's gold medals and two of the three women's.

Whitewater racing

The spectacular whitewater slalom events were first included in 1972, but reappeared only in 1992. Competitors, who set out at intervals, have to negotiate at least 20 "gates" on a winding course, some of which involve paddling upstream. Positions are determined on time (with penalties for gates missed or not taken properly) and the better time of two runs counts.

MEDALS TABLE MEN

K-1 500m		
1		
2		
3		

K-1 1000m		
1		
2		
3		

K-2 500m		
1		
2		
3		

K-2 1000m		
1		
2		
3		

K-4 1000m		
1		
2		
3		

K-1 SLALOM		
1		
2		
3		

C-1 500m		
1		
2		
3		

C-1 1000m		
1		
2		
3		

C-2 500m		
1		
2		
3		

C-2 1000m		
1		
2		
3		

C-1 SLALOM		
1		
2		
3		

C-2 SLALOM		
1		
2		
3		

MEDALS TABLE WOMEN

K-1 500m		
1		
2		
3		

K-2 500m		
1		
2		
3		

K-4 500m		
1		
2		
3		

K-1 SLALOM		
1		
2		
3		

EQUESTRIAN EVENTS

Men and women compete as equals in equestrian sport – now the only event of the Games in which this is the case – but it's the horses that catch the eye, especially in show jumping, which is one of the most popular spectator events and traditionally closes the Games.

The three equestrian disciplines are dressage, show jumping and eventing – the three-day event – which comprises the first two plus the main, cross-country phases on the second day. All three disciplines, with individual and team competitions, have been regular events at the Olympic Games since 1912, except team dressage, which was incorporated in 1928.

It was 1952 before women first took part in equestrian events. In 1956, an outbreak of equine flu in Australia meant that the equestrian events were transferred from Melbourne to Stockholm in Sweden. In the four-person team events, the best three scores count.

There was an individual show jumping event in the 1900 Games, as well as high jump and long jump contests, but there was no world governing body at this time, and rules were more or less made up on the spot. Polo twice appeared in the Games, in 1924 and 1928.

Show jumping – to a fault

The drama of the Games is never better illustrated than in the nerve-jangling final stages of the show jumping. The format of the competition is that the order for the opening round is drawn. In the second round, however, the horses jump in reverse order of their positions from the first round, meaning that the last rider to go knows that a clear round will ensure the gold medal, or at least a jump-off.

Positions in show jumping are determined by faults incurred – chiefly, 4 for a fence or part of a fence down, 4 for a foot in the water jump, 3 for a refusal, 8 for a fall and one-quarter for every second, or part thereof, by which the time allowance for the round is exceeded. If a horse refuses to jump an obstacle, the clock continues to run unless the obstacle needs repair. The two rounds of the team competition serve as qualifying rounds for the individual event, which is contested over two rounds on the final day of the Games. In the event of a tie, there is a jump-off over a shorter course against the clock.

German riders have an excellent record of success in show jumping, and other European countries among the favourites for both team and individual honours are France, Britain and the Netherlands. The USA, too, are always strong challengers.

MARK TODD (NZL) BECAME THE FIRST RIDER FOR 50 YEARS TO WIN A SECOND INDIVIDUAL GOLD IN EVENTING WHEN HE STEERED CHARISMA TO VICTORY AT BOTH LOS ANGELES IN 1984 AND SEOUL IN 1988. HE WAS WELL PLACED AT BARCELONA ON WELTON GREYLAG AFTER THE DRESSAGE TO MAKE IT AN UNPRECEDENTED HAT-TRICK, BUT THE HORSE WAS INJURED IN THE STEEPLECHASE PHASE ON THE SECOND DAY, AND PROBABLY COST NEW ZEALAND THE TEAM GOLD, TOO.

PERFECT UNDERSTANDING **Between horse and rider is vital in the tense show-jumping arena**

GERMAN 1-2-3 German riders made a clean sweep of the dressage medals in Barcelona

MEDALS TABLE INDIVIDUAL

SHOW JUMPING		
1		
2		
3		

EVENTING		
1		
2		
3		

DRESSAGE		
1		
2		
3		

MEDALS TABLE TEAM

SHOW JUMPING		
1		
2		
3		

EVENTING		
1		
2		
3		

DRESSAGE		
1		
2		
3		

Dressage – top hats and tails

Not only do women compete against men on equal terms in dressage, but they now virtually monopolize the event. Since Liselott Linsenhoff (FRG) became the first woman to win an individual equestrian gold medal, in 1972, they have failed to win the dressage only once.

In dressage, immaculately turned out riders – usually in top hat and tails – take their beautifully groomed horses through a series of precise manoeuvres and stops, demonstrating discipline, schooling and the communication between horse and rider.

Points are awarded by judges. The format of the competition has been changed so that, in Atlanta, the leading 24 from the team grand prix, take part in a special grand prix, the leading 12 of whom go on to a new freestyle grand prix, the aggregate scores determining final placings. Germany, which has been the dominant force in dressage for some time, will be hot favourites again in Atlanta, with the Netherlands expected to be their closest rivals.

Eventing – a test of endurance

Eventing begins with dressage and ends with show jumping, but these two disciplines together carry fewer points than the endurance tests of the middle event. These involve four phases, A and C being "roads and tracks" at a fast trot, B a steeplechase at a good gallop, and D the cross-country phase over all manner of fixed jumps, about 30 in all.

For Atlanta, because of the expected high temperatures, the courses have been shortened. And instead of the team and individual events being decided on the same performances, they will be separate, with different horses and riders competing.

The USA, Australasia, and Europe, particularly Britain and Germany, are eventing strongholds.

YACHTING

Although yacht racing is fought out on a remote battleground at sea, television pictures bring back the drama and excitement of dozens of yachts vying for position and the best of the wind as they speed round a buoyed course.

Seven races in seven days – ten in ten for the windsurfers – is the demanding programme for the sailors on Wassaw Sound, Georgia, in the 1996 Games.

There are 10 gold medals at stake in yachting – three each for men and women and four in open, or mixed, classes, although few women take part in these. The scoring system is based on "low points", the winner of a race recording zero points, the second 3, third 5.7, fourth 8, fifth 10, sixth 11.7, seventh 13 and one extra point for each place after seven. Each entrant discards one race, and the points for the others are added up to produce their final score.

One-class racing

Yacht racing at the Games is strictly controlled, so in each class competitors use identical equipment and the event is a test of their skill, endurance and racing know-how. Over the years, more than thirty classes have been sailed in the Olympic Games, some lasting decades, others being discarded after one or two Games as changing designs and popularity dictate.

PAUL ELVSTROM (DEN) WAS THE FIRST SPORTSMAN TO WIN FOUR SUCCESSIVE GAMES GOLD MEDALS IN AN INDIVIDUAL EVENT – A RECORD SINCE EQUALLED BY DISCUS-THROWER AL OERTER (USA) – WHEN HE WON THE FINN CLASS IN 1960. IN 1948 – HIS FIRST WIN – THIS MONOTYPE CLASS WAS KNOWN AS THE FIREFLY. HE WENT ON TO COMPETE IN A TOTAL OF SEVEN OLYMPIC GAMES SPANNING 36 YEARS, COMING FOURTH IN 1984 IN THE TORNADO CLASS PARTNERED BY HIS DAUGHTER TRINE.

There was a regatta scheduled for the first modern Olympic Games, but it was cancelled because of bad weather, so yachting did not make its début until the 1900 Games. The oldest class still in existence is the Star, now an open category, which made its first appearance in 1932. It is a keeled yacht, 6.92m (23ft) long, crewed by two people, and has the largest sail area of the classes in the Centennial Olympic Games at 26 sq m (280 sq ft). The only type of yacht that has been a permanent fixture on the programme is the one-man dinghy, which has been the Finn class since 1952.

Women at the helm

Women did not get their own event until 1988, with the 470 class. This is a centreboard dinghy (its name coming from its 4.70m – 15.4ft – length), also with a crew of two. Men have their own race in the 470 class.

Boardsailing was included in the programme for the first time in 1984. Better known, perhaps, as windsurfing, this hitherto separate sport was accorded its own women's event in 1992, when women also got their third class, the Europe, a centreboard dinghy smaller than the Finn.

One of the open classes is a catamaran, the Tornado, another category with a crew of two. The original design appeared in 1967 and the class made its début in the Olympic Games in 1976. One of the oldest classes was the Flying Dutchman – a large two-crew centreboard dinghy – but this will be replaced in 1996 with the Laser.

The longest and heaviest boat in the 1996 Games is the Soling, a keel yacht 8.16m (27ft) long and the only one with a crew of three. In 1992, best-of-three match-race finals were introduced for the first time in the Games for this class, the top four boats after six races going through to the semi-finals to battle for the medals. The country with the best record can choose their opponents, and the winners of the two semis then compete for the gold and silver, the losers for bronze and fourth place.

Buoyed up for racing

All the yacht races, except the boardsailing, take place on triangular courses marked by buoys. They allow for sailing across the wind (reaching), sailing with the wind, and tacking (zigzagging) against the wind. Tactics are a vital part of racing, such as recognizing and using shifts in the wind. Another successful ploy is to use the wind against your opponent by sailing between them and the wind – quite literally "taking the wind out of their sails".

The United States have a consistently good record in Olympic yachting as befits the virtual monopolists of the sport's most famous event, the America's Cup.

Local knowledge sometimes is of considerable help, as the Spanish sailors demonstrated at Barcelona in 1992, when they amassed four gold medals – one more than their total in all previous Games.

BOARDSAILING IN BARCELONA The biggest fleet – 44 competitors – took part in the men's event

MEDALS TABLE MEN

MISTRAL (BOARDSAILING)		
1		
2		
3		

FINN		
1		
2		
3		

470		
1		
2		
3		

MEDALS TABLE WOMEN

MISTRAL (BOARDSAILING)		
1		
2		
3		

FINN		
1		
2		
3		

470		
1		
2		
3		

MEDALS TABLE OPEN

LASER		
1		
2		
3		

TORNADO		
1		
2		
3		

STAR		
1		
2		
3		

SOLING		
1		
2		
3		

SOLING SAILORS Denmark won gold in 1992

The modern Olympic Movement was the brainchild of Baron Pierre de Coubertin, a French scholar who was inspired by the excavation of the Ancient Greek site of Olympia in the 1870s and by the tradition of sport he found in English public schools on visits to Britain.

A growing repugnance towards the commercialism of sport finally led him to seek a revival of the amateur spirit, and he was responsible in 1894 for setting up the International Olympic Committee (IOC), a self-perpetuating body that, to this day, governs the Olympic Games.

1896 Athens

BIRTH OF THE MODERN GAMES

The first of the modern Olympics were held in Athens to mark their ancient origins. Some 80,000 spectators witnessed the opening ceremony.

There were nine sports, with events only for men: athletics, cycling, fencing, gymnastics, lawn tennis, shooting, swimming, weightlifting and wrestling. Rowing was also scheduled, but was cancelled because of bad weather. Of the 311 competitors who took part, the largest contingent by far – 230 – came from the host country.

The highlight of the Games was the last event of all, the marathon. The Greeks, who had not won an athletics event, pinned their hopes on a handsome, moustachioed shepherd called Spiridon Louis. They were not disappointed. When he came home first, in just under 3 hours, he was showered with gifts and became a national hero.

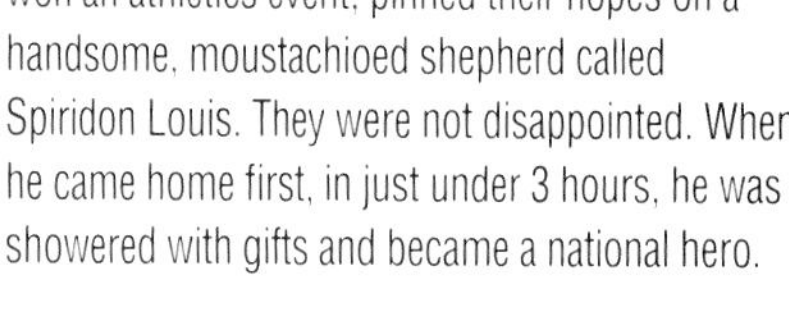

1900 Paris

TEETHING PROBLEMS

Competitors often did not know they were taking part in the Paris Olympics of 1900. The Games were held in conjunction with the World's Fair and events took place over many months.

One athlete surprised to find he had won an Olympic gold medal was Michel Theato (FRA), who won the marathon (and as a local baker's delivery man was rumoured to have taken some short cuts). Another, Margaret Abbott (USA), who won the golf tournament in Paris – this was the first Games in which women took part – died without knowing that she was the first American female Olympic champion, a fact her family discovered only in 1983.

DORANDO PIETRI'S DISQUALIFICATION **The Italian is helped over the line at the end of the Marathon**

1904 St Louis

CONFUSION CONTINUES

As with the Games four years earlier, these Olympics were held in conjunction with the World's Fair. In St Louis all the sports connected with the fair were described as "Olympic", including professional, schoolboy and other unrelated contests. It was only in retrospect, in 1912, that the IOC reconstructed the events and awarded medals. Few European nations could afford or even desired to send teams to St Louis in 1904, and as a result the Games were more like US national championships.

THE START OF SOMETHING BIG **Athletes getting set for the final of the 100m in 1896**

1906 Athens

INTERCALATED REDEMPTION

The saviour of the Olympics was an Interim, or Intercalated, Games held in Athens in 1906. The Greeks persuaded De Coubertin to sanction these Games, but they did not come under the official patronage of the IOC and were not numbered. They were well organized, well attended and paved the way for the next Olympics, in 1908.

1908 London

DISPUTES STILL ABOUND

In 1908, more than 2,000 competitors – 36 of them women – took part in 21 sports. For the first time, entry was by countries, rather than by individuals. A purpose-built stadium at the White City, in West London, had a running track inside a banked cycle track, and a swimming pool on the grass infield. Most of the sports were staged in July, but the team competitions, such as football, were held in October, as was the skating, the first winter sport to be held in the Olympics. There was also a racquets tournament, begun at the end of April, with no overseas entries.

The London Games are remembered most for the disqualification of Dorando Pietri (ITA), for receiving assistance as he staggered towards the finishing line in the marathon, and for the walkover of Wyndham Halswelle (GBR) in the 400m. The walkover occurred because two Americans refused to compete in a "rerun" of the race after the disqualification of their compatriot.

1912 Stockholm

TURNING THE CORNER

With the number of sports cut to 14 at Baron De Coubertin's insistence, the Stockholm Games produced excellent competition with few disputes. The athletics, in which forms of photo-finish and electrical timing were employed for the first time, was graced by two outstanding performers. Hannes Kolehmainen (FIN) won the 5,000m and 10,000m and the 8,000m cross-country gold medals to launch the great Finnish tradition of distance running, and Jim Thorpe (USA) won the two new all-round events, the pentathlon and decathlon.

1920 Antwerp

POST-WAR CONTRACTION

The hastily prepared Games in war-torn Belgium – Austria, Bulgaria, Germany, Hungary and Turkey were not invited – saw the reaffirmation of the Finns as "kings of distance", with Hannes Kolehmainen winning the closest ever marathon by 12.8sec and the great Paavo Nurmi making a winning début in the 10k and the cross-country. These were the first Games with the Olympic oath and Olympic flag. The first Olympic ice hockey tournament was won predictably by Canada.

JIM THORPE (USA), PART AMERICAN INDIAN, ARGUABLY THE GREATEST ALL-ROUND ATHLETE AND SPORTSMAN OF ALL TIME, WAS FORCED BY THE AMERICAN ATHLETIC UNION TO RETURN THE GOLD MEDALS HE WON IN STOCKHOLM WHEN AN INNOCENT CONTRAVENTION EARLIER IN HIS CAREER OF THE STRICT AMATEUR LAWS (PLAYING BASEBALL FOR A FEW DOLLARS) CAME TO LIGHT. HE LATER PLAYED MAJOR LEAGUE BASEBALL AND WAS A BIG PRO FOOTBALL STAR, BUT IT WAS NOT UNTIL 1982, LONG AFTER HIS DEATH, THAT HIS NAME WAS RESTORED TO THE OLYMPIC ROLL OF HONOUR AND HIS MEDALS RETURNED TO HIS FAMILY.

JESSE OWENS (USA), FOUR-GOLD HERO OF THE 1936 OLYMPICS, WENT TO BERLIN HAVING THE PREVIOUS YEAR INDULGED IN AN UNPARALLELED AFTERNOON OF RECORD-BREAKING – SIX WORLD RECORDS IN FOUR EVENTS IN THE SPACE OF BARELY 45 MINUTES ON 25 MAY. AFTER EQUALLING THE 100YD MARK, HE MADE THE FIRST EVER 8-METRE LONG-JUMP (HIS 8.13M – 26FT 8IN – LASTED 25 YEARS), AND DOUBLED UP WITH METRIC RECORDS IN THE 220YD AND 220YD HURDLES.

1924 Paris

NURMI'S OLYMPICS

The Olympics made famous by the film *Chariots of Fire* and the triumphs of British sprinters Harold Abrahams (100m) and Eric Liddell (400m), boasted another big-screen connection in the shape of Johnny Weissmuller, star of the all-conquering US swimming team, who went on to Hollywood fame and fortune as Tarzan.

Yet these Games are forever known as "Nurmi's Olympics" for the extraordinary feats of the Finnish distance runner who won five gold medals in six days.

1928 Amsterdam

THE FLAME BURNS BRIGHTLY

Described by the president of the US Olympic Committee, General Douglas MacArthur (of Second World War fame) as a model for future Olympics, the Amsterdam Games boasted a 400m track, which did indeed become an Olympic standard, a large results board, and an Olympic flame, which burned throughout the celebration. And women's athletics made its first appearance in the Games with five events.

1932 Los Angeles

PUTTING ON THE STYLE

The American authorities made up for the 1904 flop in St Louis by putting on a highly competent and competitive Games in Los Angeles, although participation was down because of the cost and time involved for European athletes.

Finland continued to dominate the distance races, and Japan proved a new force in the jumping events. The USA won five of the six women's athletics gold medals, and took six of the seven swimming and diving events, but the Japanese provided the shock of the Games by taking five of the six men's swimming golds.

1936 Berlin

OWENS'S GAMES

An extremely controversial Games, known as the "Nazi Olympics" because it was used by Hitler, Goebbels and Co. as a vast nationalistic propaganda exercise, Berlin is above all remembered for the way America's black athletes confounded the Nazi theory of Aryan supremacy – in particular, Jesse Owens's performance in winning four gold medals in track and field. The Games were, nevertheless, organized with a level of efficiency that had not been seen before.

The Games opened dramatically with a typically blond runner carrying the Olympic flame, at the culmination of the first Olympic torch relay, through 25,000 "Hitler Youth" in the centre of the new stadium lined with swastikas, in front of 100,000 spectators.

GOLDEN BABE Mildred Didrickson (USA, right) won the women's 80m hurdles gold medal in 1932

EMIL ZATOPEK (TCH), UNIVERSALLY POPULAR DISTANCE RUNNER WHOSE AGONIZED LOOK BELIED THE STRENGTH IN HIS LEGS AND POWER IN HIS LUNGS, WAS UNBEATEN IN 38 RACES OVER 10K FROM 1948 TO 1954. HE WON THE 10K AT THE 1948 OLYMPICS AND ADDED HIS UNIQUE TREBLE IN 1952, AND HE SET 18 WORLD RECORDS FROM 5K TO 30K.

1948 London

AUSTERITY OLYMPICS

In a time of austerity, the British organized a low-budget first post-war Games, which nevertheless attracted more countries (but neither the banned Germany and Japan, nor the still unaffiliated Soviet Union) and competitors than ever before. The star of the Games was a 30-year-old Dutch housewife, Fanny Blankers-Koen, who won four gold medals – 100m, 200m, hurdles, and relay – and brought joy to a drab, wet Olympic stadium with her dash and exuberance.

1952 Helsinki

ENTER THE SOVIET UNION

Although the Finns failed to reproduce their former glories on the track, it was appropriate that the star of the games was another distance runner, Emil Zatopek (TCH), who won the 5k, 10k and marathon – his wife Dana won the javelin. Heavyweight boxer Ingemar Johansson (SWE) was disqualified for not trying, while 17-year-old middleweight Floyd Patterson (USA) won gold. The Soviet Union made its first appearance at the Games (Tsarist Russia last competed in 1912).

1956 Melbourne

AUSSIE DOUBLES

Melbourne staged a hugely successful Games – the first Olympiad to be held outside of Europe or America – and enjoyed more than its share of star performances. These included the 5,000m/10,000m double of the new king of long-distance running, Vladimir Kuts (URS); sprint trebles by Betty Cuthbert (AUS) and Bobby Morrow (USA); a 400m/1500m/relay treble by Australian swimmer Murray Rose; and a double gold for the second Games running by diver Patricia McCormick (USA).

In the closing ceremony – at the suggestion of a Chinese-Australian schoolboy – competitors from all the nations mingled and marched together, a tradition that has now become one of the happiest and most popular of the Olympic celebrations.

1960 Rome

BIKILA SIGNALS NEW DAWN

The first Games to have world-wide television coverage, Rome provided ample excitement for the millions of viewers, especially on the athletics track, where Herb Elliott (AUS) completely outclassed the 1500m field in a world record time of 3min 35.6sec that stood for seven years; Armin Hary (FRG), the first man to run 10.0sec dead, won the 100m in 10.2sec; and Livio Berruti (ITA) became the first European to win the 200m, equalling the world record with 20.5sec.

Wilma Rudolph made up for the lack of American success in the men's sprints by taking both 100m and 200m and winning a third gold in the women's sprint relay. The marathon, which took the runners dramatically back along the torchlit Appian Way in the evening, was won in world-best time by barefoot sensation Abebe Bikila, a little-known Ethiopian who signalled the arrival of a new force in distance running. In other sports, Ingrid Krämer (GDR) broke a 40-year-old US monopoly of women's diving, winning both events, and a certain Cassius Clay (USA) danced and jabbed his way to a gold medal in the light-heavyweight division of the boxing.

Flying Finn Lasse Viren, despite an early fall, on his way to the gold medal and a world record in the 10,000m at Munich

1964 Tokyo

WINNING IN THE RAIN

The first Olympics to take place in Asia were well organized, but suffered from incessant rain. Bob Schul and Billy Mills won the first ever US golds in the 5,000m and 10,000m, respectively, to clinch America's greatest ever showing on the track as their men also won the sprints, the relays and the hurdles. But perhaps the finest track performance was the 800m/1500m double of Peter Snell (NZL). Abebe Bikila (ETH), wearing shoes this time, became the first marathon runner to retain his title.

Australian swimmer Dawn Fraser won her third 100m freestyle, the first woman to do this in any sport, and Soviet rower Vyacheslav Ivanov won his third successive single sculls.

1968 Mexico City

GAMES WITH ALTITUDE

A contentious choice for the Games because of its high altitude (2268m), Mexico City saw even more controversy when sprinters Tommie Smith (USA) and John Carlos (USA) gave the "Black Power" salute on the winners' rostrum and were both sent home. The thin air favoured the more "explosive" events, and long-standing records set by winners included Bob Beamon's (USA) 8.90m (29ft 2½in) long-jump, Smith's 19.8sec 200m and Lee Evans's (USA) 43.8sec 400m.

Abebe Bikila's bid for a third marathon title was thwarted by an injured leg, but Mamo Wolde made it a hat-trick for Ethiopia. Al Oerter (USA) staked his claim as the greatest Olympian of all time with his fourth discus gold medal. And Wyomia Tyus (USA) became the first sprinter of either sex to retain the 100m title.

MARK SPITZ (USA), A "FAILURE" IN 1968, AT 18, WHEN HE WON "ONLY" TWO SWIMMING RELAY GOLDS, A SILVER AND A BRONZE INSTEAD OF THE SIX GOLDS EXPECTED OF HIM, REMOVED ALL DOUBTS AS TO HIS COMPETITIVE ABILITY IN 1972, WINNING SEVEN GOLD MEDALS – THE 100M/200M FREESTYLE, 100M/200M BUTTERFLY AND THREE RELAYS, ALL IN WORLD RECORD TIMES.

1972 Munich

TERRORISM STRIKES

Overshadowing everything at Munich was the murder halfway through the Games of 11 members of the Israeli team by Arab terrorists – themselves killed attempting to escape with hostages. The IOC had earlier excluded the Rhodesian team to prevent a "black boycott". The era of political exploitation of the Olympics had arrived.

In sport, US swimmer Mark Spitz (USA) broke all Olympic records with seven gold medals in one Games, but the United States had a disappointing time, losing the pole vault and basketball titles for the first time. Perhaps the brightest moments of the Games were supplied by the young Soviet gymnast Olga Korbut, who revolutionized the sport with her cheeky, charming displays.

1976 Montreal

A NEW "FLYING FINN"

Beset by problems before the start – construction problems with the Olympic stadium have left the city in debt ever since – the Games suffered another blow when 20, mainly African, countries boycotted the Games over New Zealand's sporting relations with South Africa.

The stars of the track were Lasse Viren, who revived the glory days of Finnish distance running with his second 5,000m/10,000m double, something none of his illustrious predecessors had done, and Alberto Juantorena (CUB), who impressively achieved the first ever 400m/800m double. The 17-year-old Kornelia Ender (GDR) won four gold medals, a record for a woman swimmer, and the 14-year-old Nadia Comaneci (ROM) achieved the first ever perfect 10 mark in Olympic gymnastics – and then six more – in winning three golds, including the overall title.

OLGA KORBUT (URS) BROUGHT A NEW DIMENSION TO GYMNASTICS WHEN SHE BREEZED ON TO THE OLYMPIC SCENE AT MUNICH IN 1972 AS A 17-YEAR-OLD RESERVE, TAKING PART ONLY BECAUSE A MEMBER OF THE SOVIET TEAM FELL ILL. WITH HER ELFIN CHARM AND RADIANT PERSONALITY, SHE WON THE HEARTS OF THE SPECTATORS AND THE WATCHING MILLIONS ON TELEVISION. SHE WON MEDALS, TOO: THREE GOLDS AND A SILVER. GYMNASTICS HAS NOT BEEN THE SAME SINCE.

1980 Moscow

ABSENT FRIENDS

The Soviet incursion into Afghanistan at the end of 1979 sparked a mainly Western boycott of the Moscow Games, led by the United States. The selection of a communist country to host the Games for the first time had in itself been controversial, but the IOC stood by its decision and was determined not to let politics interfere with the staging of the Olympics.

In the end, the boycott was limited. Countries such as Britain and Australia, whose governments supported the American stand, put pressure on their National Olympic Committees to withdraw. But the NOC's showed their independence, and 81 of the 145 countries invited to take part in the Games of the twenty-second Olympiad accepted. Notable among other absentees were West Germany, Japan and Canada. Some national federations also defected, affecting the equestrian and yachting events in particular.

Middle distance battle

The abiding memories of the Games were the long-awaited clashes of two of the greatest middle-distance runners the world had seen to that time, two athletes who had not faced each other on the track since 1978, but who had been carving up the world records between them. This was no chauvinistic rivalry, though, but the meeting of two team-mates, Sebastian Coe and Steve Ovett (GBR). Under the fascinated gaze of the world, Ovett took the 800m from the favourite, Coe, who ran a tactically naïve race. But Coe came back courageously in the 1500m – Ovett's stronger distance – to share the spoils.

Miruts Yifter continued the wonderful tradition of Ethiopian long-distance running with a magnificent 10,000m/5,000m double, pulverizing the opposition with his last-lap bursts to earn the nickname "Yifter the Shifter". Other notable individual performances included boxer Teofilo Stevenson's (CUB) third successive heavyweight gold medal and the feat of Aleksandr Dityatin (URS) in winning a medal in all eight gymnastics events.

UNUSUAL DOUBLE **Ulrike Meyfarth (FRG) wins the 1984 high jump – 12 years after her first success**

Women's hockey was included for the first time, the winners being Zimbabwe, on their Olympic début.

1984 Los Angeles

MORE ABSENT FRIENDS

It was perhaps inevitable, after Moscow, that there should be a "tit-for-tat" boycott of the Los Angeles Games by Eastern Bloc countries led by the USSR. But this last-minute withdrawal still left a record 140 countries competing (out of 159 invited), including Romania.

SEBASTIAN COE (GBR) FINISHED HONOURS EVEN WITH HIS GREAT RIVAL STEVE OVETT (GBR) IN MOSCOW, BUT COE WENT ON TO REPEAT HIS 800M SILVER AND 1500M GOLD IN 1984 AT LOS ANGELES, WHERE OVETT SUFFERED FROM BREATHING PROBLEMS AND LEFT THE TRACK ON A STRETCHER. IN A 41-DAY PERIOD IN 1979, COE SET NEW WORLD MARKS FOR THE 800M, ONE MILE AND 1500M, THE FIRST ATHLETE TO HOLD THE THREE PRIME MIDDLE-DISTANCE RECORDS SIMULTANEOUSLY. IN ALL, HE ACHIEVED EIGHT WORLD RECORDS. HIS 800M MARK OF 1MIN 41.73SEC, SET IN 1981, STILL STOOD AS THE 1996 OLYMPICS APPROACHED.

SUPER HEAVYWEIGHT **In 1980 Teofilo Stevenson (CUB) won the third of his three boxing gold medals**

The loss of the Soviet Union and East Germany was felt particularly in such sports as swimming and gymnastics, but their defection took nothing away from the star of the games, Carl Lewis (USA), who emulated his compatriot Jesse Owens (1936) by winning four track and field gold medals – in the 100m, 200m, long jump and sprint relay. Valerie Brisco-Hooks (USA) also won three track golds in the 200m, 400m and relay.

Decker trips out

The most sensational incident involved another track star, US golden girl Mary Decker, who was accidentally tripped by Britain's controversial South African-born, barefoot runner Zola Budd, and went staggering out of the 3,000m, which was won by Maricica Puica (ROM).

The first ever women's Olympic marathon went to Joan Benoit (USA); Sebastian Coe (GBR) became the first runner to retain the Olympic 1500m title; pistol shooter Xu Haifeng (CHN) won that nation's first Olympic gold medal; and archer Neroli Fairhall (NZL) was the first paraplegic to compete in the Olympics.

These were the first Olympics to introduce private sponsorship, and the $215m profit was a triumph for LA's organizing committee under Peter Ueberroth.

CARL LEWIS (USA), WHOSE MEDAL HAUL IN LOS ANGELES WAS GOOD ENOUGH TO PUT HIM UP WITH THE GREATEST OLYMPIANS OF ALL TIME, WENT ON, IN THE NEXT TWO GAMES, TO EVEN GREATER ACHIEVEMENTS, WINNING FOUR MORE GOLDS – IN THE 100M (1988), LONG JUMP (BOTH) AND RELAY (1992), IN WHICH HE RAN THE FASTEST EVER ANCHOR LEG OF 8.85SEC TO HELP THE US TEAM TO A 37.40SEC WORLD RECORD. HE SET 100M WORLD RECORDS OF 9.93SEC, WHEN WINNING THE 1987 WORLD TITLE, AND 9.86SEC IN 1991 WHEN TAKING HIS THIRD WORLD CHAMPIONSHIP IN A ROW. IN ADDITION TO HIS THREE OLYMPIC LONG JUMP GOLDS, HE WON THE WORLD CHAMPIONSHIP IN 1983 AND 1987, BUT, DESPITE THREE 29FT JUMPS IN 1991, HE WAS DEPRIVED OF A THIRD WORLD TITLE WHEN MIKE POWELL (USA) BROKE BOB BEAMON'S 23-YEAR-OLD WORLD RECORD. LEWIS WILL BE 35 IN 1996.

1988 Seoul

TESTING TIME

Everything at Seoul was overshadowed by the disqualification of 100m winner Canadian Ben Johnson. The race itself was sensational; the explosive Johnson outstripped defending champion Carl Lewis (USA), and smashed his own world record with a breathtaking time of 9.79sec. But a day later came the sombre announcement from the IOC that Johnson had tested positive for stanozolol, an anabolic steroid. Johnson was disqualified, stripped of his gold medal, sent home in disgrace and had his time expunged from the records. So Lewis became the first male sprinter to retain his title in the history of the Games.

Lewis wrote himself even more indelibly into the Olympic "hall of fame" when he also retained his long jump title to take his tally of golds to six. America's women athletes were also outstanding, Florence Griffith-Joyner – "Flo-Jo" – winning both sprints and gold and silver in the relays, while her sister-in-law Jackie Joyner-Kersee won the long jump and heptathlon. All five men's track events from 800m upwards were won by Africans, four of them by Kenyans.

Two golden swimmers

The East German swimmer Kristin Otto amassed six gold medals, the biggest haul by a woman in one Games, including four individual golds encompassing an unprecedented three different strokes. In men's swimming, Matt Biondi (USA) could not quite live up to the Mark Spitz tag, but he did come away with seven medals, five of which were of the gold variety.

The boxing arrangements left much to be desired and there were some unsavoury incidents. One Korean competitor refused to

GREG LOUGANIS (USA) WAS THE HERO OF THE POOL IN SEOUL. HE NOT ONLY CROWNED HIS CAREER BY WINNING BOTH DIVING TITLES FOR THE SECOND OLYMPICS RUNNING – THE FIRST MAN IN OLYMPIC HISTORY TO ACCOMPLISH THIS FEAT – BUT HE DID SO AFTER HITTING HIS HEAD ON THE BOARD DURING THE SPRINGBOARD PRELIMINARIES AND SUSTAINING AN INJURY THAT NEEDED STITCHES. AT 16, IN 1976, HE WON THE OLYMPIC HIGH-DIVING SILVER MEDAL AND CAME SIXTH IN THE SPRINGBOARD, AND WAS FAVOURITE TO WIN BOTH IN MOSCOW BEFORE THE US BOYCOTT RUINED HIS HOPES. HE ALSO WON FIVE WORLD TITLES.

GOLDEN PAIR **The 1992 coxless pairs champions, Matthew Pinsent and, winning his third gold medal, Steven Redgrave (GBR)**

leave the ring after the verdict went against him, and remained there for 70 minutes, sitting on chairs provided by Korean officials!

Tennis returned to the Olympics after 64 years and table tennis was added to the Games. Seoul had been another controversial selection to host the Games, with threats looming from several quarters, not least from over the border in North Korea. But, apart from the boxing, the Games were well organized in a happy atmosphere – and they made a profit of $288m.

1992 Barcelona

HOMAGE TO CATALONIA

The 1992 Games saw the movement towards outright professionalism increase in momentum. Top-ranked players such as Stefan Edberg (SWE), Boris Becker (GER), Steffi Graf (GER) and Jennifer Capriati (USA) appeared in the tennis tournament, and in the basketball the USA were allowed to field their "Dream Team" of multi-millionaires – Larry Bird, Michael Jordan, Magic Johnson and company – who duly walked away with the gold medal without ever being extended on the court.

A record 169 countries took part in Barcelona, with 9,364 competitors, more than 10 percent up on the Seoul record. With the break-up of the Eastern Bloc, there were many "new" countries. Russia and most of the former Soviets competed as the Unified Team (EUN), and finished top of the unofficial medals table. The Baltic states competed in their own right, as did Croatia. Cuba returned to the Games and won 14 golds, to finish fifth, just below China, who showed they were rapidly becoming a major force. Germany competed as one country again, and won 33 golds. And South Africa were finally allowed back into the Olympic Movement.

A triumph of organization

The city's resources were stretched to their limits. But Barcelona's organizers carried it off efficiently and with no little style, producing a memorable Games. Nevertheless, the general consensus was that the Olympics had reached saturation point, and could no longer go on expanding.

The Games were a triumph, too, for the Spanish team, who rose to the occasion as hosts and produced 13 gold-medal winners, nine more than they had won in total in the 16 previous Games they had taken part in. Spain's King, Juan Carlos, was a good luck talisman, appearing at the vital moment to add his cheers to a home athlete.

The individual heroes of the Games included the Belarussian gymnast Vitaly Scherbo (EUN), who won six gold medals; the British oarsman Steven Redgrave, who won a gold in the coxless pairs for the third consecutive Games; and the indestructible Carl Lewis (USA), who won his third long jump title and another in the sprint relay to take his Olympic tally to a magnificent eight gold medals.

TENNIS ACE **Jennifer Capriati (USA) beat Steffi Graf (GER) in the women's tennis final in 1992**

JAN-OVE WALDNER (SWE) PREVENTED A CHINESE CLEAN-SWEEP IN THE TABLE TENNIS WHEN HE TOOK THE GOLD MEDAL IN THE MEN'S SINGLES, BEATING ANOTHER EUROPEAN, PHILIPPE GATIEN (FRA) 21–10, 21–18, 25–23 IN THE FINAL. WALDNER, WHO WAS WORLD CHAMPION IN 1989, LOST ONLY ONE GAME IN THE TOURNAMENT.

OLYMPIC GAMES RECORDS

Athletics and swimming are virtually the only sports where absolute standards may be measured, and such is the continuous improvement in performance that only one Olympic record made before 1980 has survived to Atlanta – Bob Beamon's remarkable long jump made at high altitude in 1968 at Mexico City.

RECORD BREAKERS USA men set a new world record in the 1992 4 x 400m relay

THE RECORD HOLDERS

ATHLETICS

Men

Event	Record	Holder (Country)	Year
100m	9.92s	Carl Lewis (USA)	1988
200m	19.73s (Not made in final)	Michael Marsh (USA)	1992
400m	43.50s	Quincy Watts (USA)	1992
800m	1m43.00s	Joaquim Cruz (BRA)	1984
1500m	3m32.53s	Sebastian Coe (GBR)	1984
5.000m	13m5.59s	Saïd Aouita (MAR)	1984
10.000m	27m21.46s	Brahim Boutayeb (MAR)	1988
Marathon	2h9m21s	Carlos Lopes (POR)	1984
110m Hurdles	12.98s	Roger Kingdom (USA)	1988
400m Hurdles	46.78s	Kevin Young (USA)	1992
3.000m Steeplechase	8m5.51s	Julius Kariuki (KEN)	1988
4 x 100m Relay	37.40s	United States	1992
4 x 400m Relay	2m55.74s	United States	1992
20km Walk	1h19m57s	Jozef Pribilinec (TCH)	1988
50km Walk	3h38m29s	Vyacheslav Ivanenko (URS)	1988
High Jump	2.38m	Gennadiy Avdeyenko (URS)	1988
Pole Vault	5.90m	Sergey Bubka (URS)	1988
Long Jump	8.90m	Bob Beamon (USA)	1968
Triple Jump	17.63m	Mike Conley (USA)	1992
Shot Put	22.47m	Ulf Timmermann (GDR)	1988
Discus Throw	68.82m	Jürgen Schult (GDR)	1988
Hammer Throw	84.80m	Sergey Litvinov (URS)	1988
Javelin Throw	89.66m	Jan Zelezny (TCH)	1992
Decathlon	8847pts	Daley Thompson (GBR)	1984

Women

Event	Record	Holder (Country)	Year
100m	10.62s (Not made in final)	Florence Griffith-Joyner (USA)	1988
200m	21.34s	Florence Griffith-Joyner (USA)	1988
400m	48.65s	Olga Bryzgina (URS)	1988
800m	1m53.43s	Nadezhda Olizarenko (URS)	1980
1500m	3m53.96s	Paula Ivan (ROM)	1988
5.000m	New event 1996		
10.000m	31m5.21s	Olga Bondarenko (URS)	1988
Marathon	2h24m52s	Joan Benoit (USA)	1984
100m Hurdles	12.38s	Yordanka Donkova (BUL)	1988
400m Hurdles	53.17s	Debbie Flintoff-King (AUS)	1988
4 x 100m Relay	41.60s	East Germany	1980
4 x 400m Relay	3m15.18s	USSR	1988
10km Walk	44m32s	Chen Yueling (CHN)	1992
High Jump	2.03m	Louise Ritter (USA)	1988
Long Jump	7.40m	Jackie Joyner-Kersee (USA)	1988
Triple Jump	New event 1996		
Shot Put	22.41m	Ilona Slupianek (GDR)	1980
Discus Throw	72.30m	Martina Hellmann (GDR)	1988
Javelin Throw	74.68m	Petra Felke (GDR)	1988
Heptathlon	7291pts	Jackie Joyner-Kersee (USA)	1988

SWIMMING

Men

Event	Record	Holder (Country)	Year
50m Freestyle	21.90s	Alexandr Popov (EUN)	1992
100m Freestyle	48.63s	Matt Biondi (USA)	1988
200m Freestyle	1m46.70s	Yevgeniy Sadoviy (EUN)	1992
400m Freestyle	3m45.00s	Yevgeniy Sadoviy (EUN)	1992
1500m Freestyle	14m43.48s	Kieren Perkins (AUS)	1992
100m Backstroke	53.98s	Mark Tewksbury (CAN)	1992
200m Backstroke	1m58.47s	Martin López-Zubero (ESP)	1992
100m Breaststroke	1m1.50s	Nelson Diebel (USA)	1992
200m Breaststroke	2m10.16s	Mike Barrowman (USA)	1992
100m Butterfly	53.00s	Anthony Nesty (SUR)	1988
200m Butterfly	1m56.26s	Melvin Stewart (USA)	1992
200m Individual Medley	2m0.17s	Tamas Darnyi (HUN)	1988
400m Individual Medley	4m14.23s	Tamas Darnyi (HUN)	1992
4 x 100m Freestyle Relay	3m16.53s	United States	1988
4 x 200m Freestyle Relay	7m11.95s	Unified Team	1992
4 x 100m Medley Relay	3m36.93s	United States	1988 & 1992

SWIMMING

Women

Event	Record	Holder (Country)	Year
50m Freestyle	24.79s	Yang Wenyi (CHN)	1992
100m Freestyle	54.64s	Zhuang Yong (CHN)	1992
200m Freestyle	1m57.65s	Heike Friedrich (GDR)	1988
400m Freestyle	4m3.85s	Janet Evans (USA)	1988
800m Freestyle	8m20.20s	Janet Evans (USA)	1988
100m Backstroke	1m0.68s	Krisztina Egerszegi (HUN)	1992
200m Backstroke	2m7.06s	Krisztina Egerszegi (HUN)	1992
100m Breaststroke	1m7.95s	Tania Dangalakova (BUL)	1988
200m Breaststroke	2m26.65s	Kyoko Iwasaki (JAP)	1992
100m Butterfly	58.62s	Qian Hong (CHN)	1992
200m Butterfly	2m6.90s	Mary T.Meagher (USA)	1984
200m Individual Medley	2m11.65s	Lin Li (CHN)	1992
400m Individual Medley	4m36.29s	Petra Schneider (GDR)	1980
4 x 100m Freestyle Relay	3m39.46s	United States	1992
4 x 200m Freestyle Relay	New event 1996		
4 x 100m Medley Relay	4m2.54s	United States	1992

IN THE SWIM Janet Evans (USA) set records in both the 400m and 800m freestyle in 1988

OTHER NOTABLE FACTS AND FEATS

MOST GOLD MEDALS	Men	10 Ray Ewry* (USA) Athletics 1900–08
		9 Paavo Nurmi (FIN) Athletics 1920–28
		9 Mark Spitz (USA) Swimming 1968–72
	Women	9 Larissa Latynina (URS) Gymnastics 1956–64
MOST MEDALS	Women	18 Larissa Latynina (URS) Gymnastics 1956–64
	Men	15 Nikolay Andrianov (URS) Gymnastics 1972–80
MOST GOLD MEDALS IN ONE GAMES	Men	7 Mark Spitz (USA) Swimming 1972
	Women	6 Kristin Otto (GDR) Swimming 1988
MOST MEDALS IN ONE GAMES	Men	8 Alexandr Ditiatin (URS) Gymnastics 1980
	Women	7 Maria Gorokhovskaya† (URS) Gymnastics 1952
MOST GOLD MEDALS IN ONE EVENT	Men	4 Paul Elvström (DEN) Monotype Yachting 1948–60
		4 Al Oerter (USA) Discus 1956–68
	Women	3 Dawn Fraser (AUS) 100m Freestyle Swimming 1956–64
		3 Larissa Latynina‡ (URS) Gymnastics Floor Exercises 1956–64

* All for the long-defunct standing jumps (high, long and triple) and including two in the Intercalated Games of 1906.

† Including a silver in the Team Exercise with Portable Apparatus (held only in 1952 and 1956), a forerunner of Rhythmic Gymnastics.

‡ Including one shared (1956).

CELEBRATIONS OF THE OLYMPIC GAMES*

No.	Year	Venue	Period	Nations	Men	Women	Total
I	1896	Athens, Greece	†6 – 15 April	14	211	–	211
II	1900	Paris, France	20 May – 28 Oct	26	1206	19	1225
III	1904	St Louis, USA	1 Jul – 23 Nov	13	681	6	687
**	1906	Athens, Greece	22 Apr – 2 May	20	820	6	826
IV	1908	London, Gt Britain	27 Apr – 31 Oct	22	1999	36	2035
V	1912	Stockholm, Sweden	5 May – 22 Jul	28	2490	57	2547
VI	1916	Berlin	Not held				
VII	1920	Antwerp, Belgium	20 Apr – 12 Sep	29	2591	77	2668
VIII	1924	Paris, France	4 May – 27 Jul	44	2956	136	3092
IX	1928	Amsterdam, Holland	17 May – 12 Aug	46	2724	290	3014
X	1932	Los Angeles, USA	30 Jul – 14 Aug	37	1281	127	1408
XI	1936	Berlin, Germany	1 – 16 Aug	49	3738	328	4066
XII	1940	Tokyo, then Helsinki	Not held				
XIII	1944	London	Not held				
XIV	1948	London, Gt Britain	29 Jul – 14 Aug	59	3714	385	4099
XV	1952	Helsinki, Finland	19 Jul – 3 Aug	69	4407	518	4925
XVI	1956	Melbourne, Australia‡	22 Nov – 8 Dec	67	2813	371	3184
XVII	1960	Rome, Italy	25 Aug – 11 Sep	83	4736	610	5346
XVIII	1964	Tokyo, Japan	10 – 24 Oct	93	4457	683	5140
XIX	1968	Mexico City, Mexico	12 – 27 Oct	112	4749	781	5530
XX	1972	Munich, W.Germany	26 Aug – 10 Sep	121	6065	1058	7123
XXI	1976	Montreal, Canada	17 Jul – 1 Aug	92	4781	1247	6028
XXII	1980	Moscow, USSR	19 Jul – 3 Aug	80	4093	1124	5217
XXIII	1984	Los Angeles, USA	28 Jul – 12 Aug	140	5230	1567	6797
XXIV	1988	Seoul, S.Korea	17 Sep – 2 Oct	159	6279	2186	8465
XXV	1992	Barcelona, Spain	25 Jul – 9 Aug	169	6657	2707	9364
XXVI	1996	Atlanta, USA	19 Jul – 4 Aug		§6582	§3779	§10,788
XXVII	2000	Sydney, Australia	15 Sep – 1 Oct¶				

* Updated statistics provided by the International Society of Olympic Historians from the latest research.
** This celebration, to mark the 10th anniversary of the modern Games, was officially intercalated, but not numbered.
† Actually March 25 – April 3 by the Julian Calendar then in use in Greece.
‡ Equestrian events held in Stockholm, Sweden, June 10–17, with 158 competitors (145 men, 13 women) from 29 countries.
§ Estimated figures; the total includes 427 competitors in equestrian and open yachting events, who may be either male or female.
¶ Provisional dates.

Let the Games begin

The athletes of the world have paraded round the Olympic Stadium. The Olympic Torch has been lit. The doves of peace have been released. Atlanta Olympic Games . . . the heat is on!

Picture Acknowledgements

The publishers would like to thank the following sources for their kind permission to reproduce the images in this book:

Allsport/Shaun Botterill, Clive Brunskill, Simon Bruty, David Cannon, Chris Cole, Tony Duffy, Mike Hewitt, David Leah, Bob Martin, Richard Martin, Clive Mason, James Meehan, Mike Powell, Gary M Prior, Ben Radford, Vandystadt, Anton Want; **Allsport/USA/** Markus Boesch, Rich Clarskson; **Norman Barrett Collection**; **Colorsport/** Chefnourry, Andrew Cowie, duomo, Stewart Fraser, Gronik, F.Haslin, Live Action, Pica Pressfoto, Ruszniewski, Sipa/Guibbaud, Tempsport; **Images Colour Library**; **Range/Bettmann**; **Rex Features**/Mark Brewer.